# CIVICS ACTIVITY BOOK

## National, State, and Local Studies

Name: _____

Date: _____

State: _____

County: _____
(parish in Louisiana; borough in Alaska)

City/town: _____
(local area)

## CONTENTS

**National** ............................................................. 7

Symbols • Flag Etiquette • Patriotic Documents ........ 8
The Constitution at a Glance ..................................... 15

**State** ................................................................. 33

Location • Symbols ..................................... 36
Geography ................................................. 43
History ...................................................... 58
Government ............................................... 62

**Local** ................................................................. 67

County ...................................................... 69
Geography ................................................. 71
City/Town .................................................. 78
History ...................................................... 81

**State Profiles** (for use with State Studies) ..................... 85

A Beka Book®
A MINISTRY OF
PENSACOLA CHRISTIAN COLLEGE
PENSACOLA, FLORIDA 32523-9160

D1501097

# INTRODUCTION

How much do you know about our nation? What about your state, your county, parish, or borough, and your city or local area? Sometimes we take for granted the freedoms and beauty that we enjoy as Americans, but if you take the time to investigate, you will find much to appreciate and admire. *Civics Activity Book* is designed to help you learn more about the government our Founding Fathers established and about that part of our great country that you call "home."

## Collecting Information

Research is fun and educational. Before you begin to gather information for your *Civics Activity Book,* look at pages 7–83 to get an idea of the kinds of information you will need to find. Your most valuable resource will be an **encyclopedia.** Check libraries for encyclopedias, almanacs, atlases, travel books, and books about your region. Also refer to **State Profiles** (pages 85–110) for general information on your state. For local information, consult your **telephone directory.** Other sources of information include your class notes, state and local museums, local travel agents, and your parents, grandparents, and neighbors.

## Completing the Activity Pages

Use the information you collect in class and from other sources to fill in the pages of this activity book as completely as possible.

Some of the pages provide space for illustrations. You may use **illustrations** from travel brochures and magazines, or you might choose to draw some illustrations yourself.

As you prepare **maps** of your state and local area, follow the guidelines suggested below.

1. Trace the map from an atlas or some other source on typing paper. Draw political borders and any major rivers or lakes. Mark the capital with a star and major cities with a dot.
2. Color your map. Shade wooded areas, grasslands, bodies of water, and desert regions with appropriate colors. Be sure to use light colors so your labels will be readable.
3. Add other important locations such as parks, railways, mountains, canals, and other features. Some of the most common map symbols are suggested in the following key.

*A Beka Book,* a Christian textbook ministry affiliated with Pensacola Christian College, is designed to meet the need for Christian textbooks and teaching aids. The purpose of this publishing ministry is to help Christian schools reach children and young people for the Lord and train them in the Christian way of life.

Maps on pages 5, 32, 33, were developed using Mountain High Map Frontiers™, Copyright © 1994 Digital Wisdom, Inc.

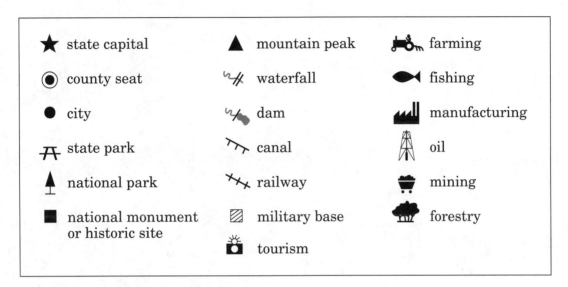

4. Label the political and physical features of your map neatly, and check your spelling carefully.
5. Mount your maps on the pages provided.

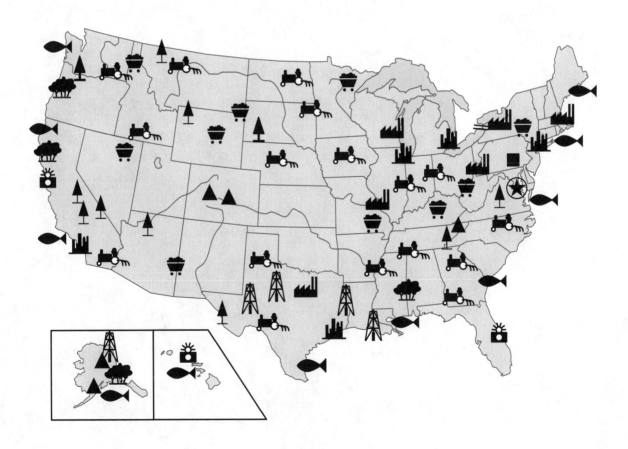

# PART ONE

The United States of America

# National Study

# CONTENTS

Introduction ...................................................... 7

National Symbols ............................................. 8

Flag Etiquette .................................................. 10

Patriotic Documents ....................................... 12

The Constitution at a Glance ...................... 15

   The Preamble ............................................... 15
   Articles 1–3, Separation of Powers .......................... 15
   Article 4, Federalism ...................................... 19
   Articles 5–7 ............................................... 20
   Amendments 1–10, The Bill of Rights ..................... 20
   Amendments 11–27 ....................................... 22
   How a Bill Becomes a Law ................................. 23

Executive Officials ......................................... 24

Legislative Officials ....................................... 30

Supreme Court Justices ................................. 31

# MY COUNTRY: THE UNITED STATES OF AMERICA

Capital: _____
(city)

Constitution of the United States: _____
(date)

Area: _____ sq. mi.    Population: _____

Rank in area: _____    Rank in population: _____
(among the nations of the world)              (among the nations of the world)

What makes my country special: _____

_____

_____

_____

_____

_____

_____

_____

_____

_____

_____

_____

_____

_____

_____

_____

# NATIONAL SYMBOLS

**Motto:** ***In God We Trust,***
  adopted July 30, 1956

**Bird:** ***Bald eagle***
  adopted June 20, 1782

**Flower:** ***Rose,***
  adopted Oct. 7, 1986

**Anthem:** ***"The Star-Spangled Banner"***
  by Francis Scott Key, adopted March 3, 1931

Oh, say can you see by the dawn's early light
  What so proudly we hailed at the twilight's last gleaming?
Whose broad stripes and bright stars thru the perilous fight,
  O'er the ramparts, we watched were so gallantly streaming?
And the rocket's red glare, the bombs bursting in air,
  'Gave proof through the night that our flag was still there.
Oh, say does that star-spangled banner yet wave
  O'er the land of the free and the home of the brave?

## Other symbols:

**United States Flag:** Our nation's best-known symbol is without question her flag, known as the "Stars and Stripes" and "Old Glory." The flag of the United States has thirteen alternating red and white stripes and fifty white stars on a blue field. The thirteen stripes represent the original thirteen states; the fifty stars represent the fifty states that make up the union today. The Stars and Stripes should inspire patriotism and love of country in every American heart.

**Statue of Liberty:** The Statue of Liberty symbolizes the freedom and opportunity that America has offered newcomers since its discovery. The people of France presented the United States with the Statue of Liberty on July 4, 1884, as a gift of goodwill.

Between 1892 and 1954, "Lady Liberty" welcomed over 12 million immigrants to New York Harbor. Americans celebrated her restoration on July 4, 1986, the 100th anniversary of the statue's completion.

**Liberty Bell:** The Liberty Bell symbolizes the War of Independence and the freedom our forefathers fought and died for. On it, the words of Leviticus 25:10 are recorded: "Proclaim liberty throughout all the land unto all the inhabitants thereof." The bell can still be seen in Philadelphia, where its peal announced the Declaration of Independence in 1776.

# FLAG ETIQUETTE

**1** ***The flag should always be***

- to the right of other flags

- to the right in crossed flags (staff in front)

- to the right of a platform

- to the right of the audience—if it is not on the platform

**2** ***Always salute the flag***
- as it goes by in a parade.
- as it is being raised or lowered.
- when singing "The Star-Spangled Banner."
- when saying the Pledge of Allegiance.

**3** ***To salute the flag:***
Stand at attention. Place your right hand over your heart. Men wearing hats remove their hats with the right hand and place them over the heart, toward the left shoulder. People in the armed services salute the flag as they would an officer.

**4** *Always raise the flag briskly and lower it slowly.* Be sure it is free to hang loose and not tangled in the rope.

**5** Always hang the flag so that the end nearest the **union** (the blue field) is attached securely but the rest of the flag is loose and free.

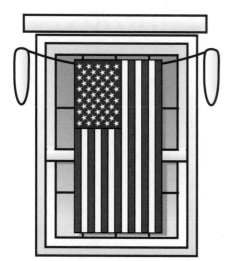

**6** Always put the union near the top when the flag is flown vertically or north if it is flown horizontally to the ground. *(An upside-down flag means a serious emergency.)*

**7** Keep the flag folded properly when it is not displayed. Fold it double; then make triangular folds starting from the striped end.

**8** *Never let the flag touch the ground.*

**9** Never use the flag for any other purpose than to represent our country. Never use it to cover objects, decorate objects or clothing, or to carry things.

**10** Display the flag only in good weather, unless it is an all-weather flag. If displayed at night it must have a spotlight shining on it.

**11** If a flag becomes unusable, it should be burned by itself in a separate container in a dignified manner.

# The Mayflower Compact

In the name of God, Amen. We whose names are under-written, the loyal subjects of our dread sovereign Lord, King James, by the grace of God, of Great Britain, France, and Ireland king, defender of the faith, etc. Having undertaken, for the glory of God, and advancement of the Christian faith, and honour of our king and country, a voyage to plant the first colony in the Northern parts of Virginia, do by these presents solemnly and mutually in the presence of God, and one of another, covenant, and combine ourselves together into a civil body politic, for our better ordering and preservation and furtherance of the ends aforesaid; and by virtue hereof to enact, constitute, and frame such just and equal laws, ordinances, acts, constitutions, and offices, from time to time, as shall be thought most meet and convenient for the general good of the colony, unto which we promise all due submission and obedience.

# Preamble to the Constitution

We the people of the United States, in order to form a more perfect Union, establish justice, insure domestic tranquillity, provide for the common defense, promote the general welfare, and secure the blessings of liberty to ourselves and our posterity, do ordain and establish this Constitution for the United States of America.

# First Amendment to the Constitution

Congress shall make no law respecting an establishment of religion, or prohibiting the free exercise thereof; or abridging the freedom of speech, or of the press; or the right of the people peaceably to assemble, and to petition the government for a redress of grievances.

# THE DECLARATION OF INDEPENDENCE

## In Congress, July 4, 1776

When, in the course of human events, it becomes necessary for one people to dissolve the political bands which have connected them with another, and to assume, among the powers of the earth, the separate and equal station to which the laws of nature and of nature's God entitle them, a decent respect to the opinions of mankind requires that they should declare the causes which impel them to the separation.

We hold these truths to be self-evident:—That all men are created equal; that they are endowed by their Creator with certain unalienable rights; that among these are life, liberty, and the pursuit of happiness. That, to secure these rights, governments are instituted among men, deriving their just powers from the consent of the governed; that, whenever any form of government becomes destructive of these ends, it is the right of the people to alter or to abolish it, and to institute a new government, laying its foundation on such principles, and organising its powers in such form, as to them shall seem most likely to effect their safety and happiness. Prudence, indeed, will dictate that governments long established should not be changed for light and transient causes; and, accordingly, all experience hath shown that mankind are more disposed to suffer, while evils are sufferable, than to right themselves by abolishing the forms to which they are accustomed. But, when a long train of abuses and usurpations, pursuing invariably the same object, evinces a design to reduce them under absolute despotism, it is their right, it is their duty, to throw off such government, and to provide new guards for their future security. . . .

# Lincoln's Gettysburg Address

Fourscore and seven years ago our fathers brought forth upon this continent a new nation, conceived in liberty, and dedicated to the proposition that all men are created equal.

Now we are engaged in a great civil war, testing whether that nation, or any nation so conceived and so dedicated, can long endure. We are met on a great battlefield of that war. We have come to dedicate a portion of that field as a final resting place for those who here gave their lives that that nation might live. It is altogether fitting and proper that we should do this.

But, in a larger sense, we cannot dedicate—we cannot consecrate—we cannot hallow—this ground. The brave men, living and dead, who struggled here, have consecrated it far above our poor power to add or detract. The world will little note nor long remember what we say here, but it can never forget what they did here. It is for us, the living, rather, to be dedicated here to the unfinished work which they who fought here have thus far so nobly advanced. It is rather for us to be here dedicated to the great task remaining before us—that from these honored dead we take increased devotion to that cause for which they gave the last full measure of devotion; that we here highly resolve that these dead shall not have died in vain; that this nation, under God, shall have a new birth of freedom; and that government of the people, by the people, for the people, shall not perish from the earth.

# THE CONSTITUTION AT A GLANCE

The Constitution of the United States, the supreme law of the land, sets forth our nation's fundamental laws. It establishes the form of the national government, defines the responsibilities and freedoms of the American people, and lists the aims of the government and the methods of achieving these aims. It is the duty of every citizen of the United States to be familiar with the Constitution and with the workings of the federal government.

The United States is a **Constitutional Republic—*a nation in which the people elect representatives to rule according to laws in their written constitution.*** Our nation was founded by people who understood human nature and were firmly convinced of the importance of law and order.

## The Preamble

The ***Preamble*** (introduction) to the Constitution states six purposes for which the United States government was established.

1. ***To form a more perfect union.***
2. ***To establish justice*** (righteousness).
3. ***To ensure domestic tranquillity*** (peace, order, and obedience to law within the nation).
4. ***To provide for the common defense.***
5. ***To promote the general welfare*** (the good of all).
6. ***To secure*** (make safe) ***the blessings of liberty to ourselves and our posterity.***

## Articles 1–3, Separation of Powers

The first three articles of the Constitution provide for a separation of powers among ***three branches*** within the national government. These articles describe how the members of the three branches of the federal government are chosen, how long they shall serve, and what qualifications they must have for office.

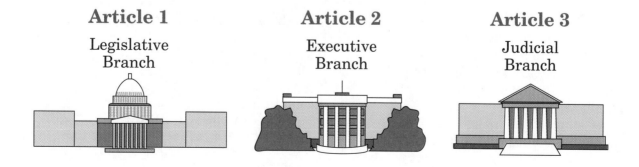

| **Article 1** | **Article 2** | **Article 3** |
|:---:|:---:|:---:|
| Legislative Branch | Executive Branch | Judicial Branch |

# The Three Branches of Government (Articles 1, 2, 3)

## 1. Legislative (Article 1; Amendments 16, 17, 20, 27)
Makes laws

### Structure
A Congress of two houses:

| *Senate* | *House of Representatives* |
|---|---|
| • two from each state (There are 100 senators today.) | • number based on state population (There are 435 representatives today.) |
| • represent state as a whole | • each represents a certain district |
| • elected for *6-year terms* | • elected for *2-year terms* |
| • Only 1/3 are up for election during an election year. | • all 435 are up for election during an election year |
| • must be **(1)** at least 30 years old, **(2)** a resident of the United States for at least 9 years, and **(3)** a resident of the state which elects him. | • must be **(1)** at least 25 years old, **(2)** a resident of the United States for at least 7 years, and **(3)** a resident of the state which elects him. |
| • presided over by ***President of the Senate*** (the Vice President) | • presided over by ***Speaker of the House*** |

### Separate Powers

| *The Senate . . .* | *The House . . .* |
|---|---|
| • may approve all treaties and appointments made by the President | • may initiate money bills (though the Senate can add amendments and *riders,* or unrelated additions) |
| • may try impeached officials | • may bring charges of impeachment (accusations) against elected officials |
| • may elect a Vice President if no candidate receives a majority of the electoral votes | • may elect a President if no candidate receives a majority of the electoral votes |

### Shared Responsibilities

*The two houses . . .*

- make laws
- impose and collect taxes
- appropriate and borrow money
- approve treaties and appointments
- regulate commerce
- coin money
- set standard for weights and measures
- set up the national court system
- establish patent and copyright regulations
- maintain the armed forces
- declare war
- govern District of Columbia
- maintain Library of Congress
- supervise Government Printing Office, General Accounting Office, the Congressional Budget Office, and other departments

## 2. Executive (Article 2; Amendments 12, 22, 25)
### Carries out laws

### Structure

| **President** (the chief executive) | **Vice President** |
|---|---|
| • must be **(1)** a natural born citizen who has **(2)** resided in the United States for at least 14 years and is **(3)** at least 35 years old. | • must meet the same qualifications as the President |
| • elected for a **4-year term** | • elected for a **4-year term** |
| • may run for a second term | **Executive Assistants** |
| • if he dies, resigns, or is impeached, the Vice President becomes President. | • appointed by the President (including the President's Cabinet and various administrative agencies.) |

### Presidential Powers

- may *veto* legislation
- may issue executive orders
- may *recall Congress* for special session
- may appeal to the people for support of legislation
- may pardon persons convicted of crimes against the national government or delay their punishment, except in cases of impeachment
- may enforce or refuse to enforce federal court decisions

### Presidential Responsibilities

- enforces laws
- appoints federal judges and other important government officials
- commands the armed forces
- serves as ceremonial head of the government
- makes official state visits to foreign countries and receives visiting chiefs of state at the White House
- determines foreign policy
- negotiates treaties with foreign countries

## 3. Judicial (Article 3; Amendment 11)
### Interprets laws

### Structure

| **Supreme Court** | **Lower Federal Courts** |
|---|---|
| • made up of a Chief Justice and 8 Associate Justices appointed by the President and approved by the Senate | • 96 District Courts, 12 Circuit Courts of Appeals, and several special courts. |
| • appointed for life; can be removed only by impeachment | |

### Powers and Responsibilities

- interprets laws
- tries cases involving the Constitution, national laws, and treaties
- also tries cases involving disagreements between **(1)** the U.S. government and other foreign governments and officials, **(2)** between states, **(3)** between citizens of different states, **(4)** between citizens of the same state who claim the same land granted to them by different states, **(5)** between a state or its resident and a foreign country or its residents

# Checks and Balances

The Constitution also provides for a *system of checks and balances* that allows the three independent branches to exert restraints upon each other. Restraints are also placed upon the national government, on the states, and on the people.

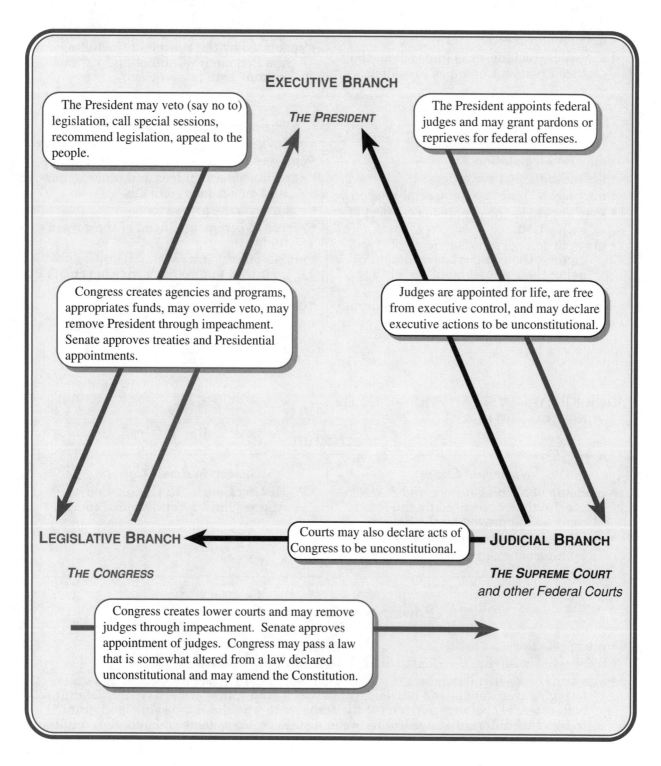

**EXECUTIVE BRANCH**

*THE PRESIDENT*

The President may veto (say no to) legislation, call special sessions, recommend legislation, appeal to the people.

The President appoints federal judges and may grant pardons or reprieves for federal offenses.

Congress creates agencies and programs, appropriates funds, may override veto, may remove President through impeachment. Senate approves treaties and Presidential appointments.

Judges are appointed for life, are free from executive control, and may declare executive actions to be unconstitutional.

**LEGISLATIVE BRANCH**

*THE CONGRESS*

Courts may also declare acts of Congress to be unconstitutional.

**JUDICIAL BRANCH**

*THE SUPREME COURT*
*and other Federal Courts*

Congress creates lower courts and may remove judges through impeachment. Senate approves appointment of judges. Congress may pass a law that is somewhat altered from a law declared unconstitutional and may amend the Constitution.

# Article 4, Federalism

In addition to separating powers within the national government, the Constitution set up a system of *federalism*, or a division of the power between the *national* government and the *state* governments. Article 4 of the Constitution outlines the relationships between states and between the national government and the states. The Constitution delegates certain powers to the national government, reserves other powers for state governments, and gives some powers to both.

## Distribution of Governmental Powers

| **National Government** (delegated powers) | **National and State** (shared powers) | **State Government** (reserved powers) |
| --- | --- | --- |
| • Regulate interstate and foreign commerce<br>• Make citizenship laws<br>• Coin money<br>• Set weights and measures<br>• Regulate copyrights and patents<br>• Establish lower courts<br>• Declare war<br>• Establish and support armed forces<br>• Admit new states | • Collect taxes<br>• Borrow money<br>• Set criminal laws<br>• Charter banks<br>• Take property for public purposes (eminent domain)<br>• Establish courts | • Regulate voting laws and procedures<br>• Establish and maintain public education<br>• Make marriage and divorce laws<br>• Make corporation laws<br>• Make traffic laws<br>• Regulate intrastate commerce<br>• Grant return of criminals and suspects |

*Jefferson Memorial*

- *Article 5*  provides for making changes, or amendments to the Constitution.
- *Article 6*  establishes that the Constitution is the supreme law of the land, to which all judges and federal and state officers are bound.
- *Article 7*  sets forth the manner in which the Constitution was to be adopted.

## Amendments 1–10, The Bill of Rights

The first 10 amendments to the Constitution, known as the Bill of Rights, were adopted in 1791.  These amendments guarantee certain rights and freedoms to the American people.

### Bill of Rights at a Glance

#### At Home and in the Community

*We are exempt from:*
- unreasonable or unwarranted searches and seizures of persons, houses, papers, and effects
- the taking of property for public use without just compensation
- the quartering of soldiers in our homes

*We are entitled to:*
- worship as we think right
- speak freely
- assemble peaceably
- keep and bear arms

#### In a Court of Law

*We are exempt from:*
- being tried twice for the same offense
- bearing witness against ourselves
- excessive bail
- excessive fines
- infliction of cruel and unusual punishments

*We are entitled to:*
- petition for redress of grievances
- due process of law regarding life, liberty, and property
- speedy public trial by impartial jury
- be informed of the nature and cause of an accusation against us
- confront any witnesses against us
- obtain witnesses in our favor
- assistance of counsel for defense

# Rights and Responsibilities
## of the American People

Along with the privileges we enjoy as Americans go important responsibilities. Some of the rights and responsibilities of American citizens as understood by our Founding Fathers are listed below.

| Right | Responsibility |
|---|---|
| • freedom to worship | • honor God with our worship and our lives |
| • freedom of speech | • speak honestly and purely; respect the opinions of others |
| • freedom of press | • keep informed and analyze what we read; do not print things that would harm others |
| • freedom to vote | • vote faithfully and wisely for what is best for the country |
| • freedom to own property | • be good stewards of our possessions; respect the property of others |
| • freedom to earn a living in one's chosen vocation | • take advantage of our educational opportunities; develop good work habits; be responsible employees |
| • freedom of assembly | • meet with others to share ideas; recognize un-American and anti-Christian activities and emotions and avoid them |

Although thousands of amendments have been introduced into Congress over the years, only 17 have been adopted since the passage of the Bill of Rights in 1791, for a total of 27.

### Amendment 11
States may not be sued in federal courts by out-of-state parties
1795

### Amendment 12
Separate ballots for President and Vice President
1804

### Amendment 13
Abolition of slavery
1865

### Amendment 14
Citizenship to black Americans
1868

### Amendment 15
Voting rights (suffrage) for black Americans
1870

### Amendment 16
Income tax
1913

### Amendment 17
Popular election of senators
1913

### Amendment 18
National prohibition of the manufacture, sale, and transportation of alcoholic beverages
1919

### Amendment 19
Suffrage for women
1920

### Amendment 20
Abolition of lame duck sessions of Congress (short sessions held after an election before new officeholders take over)
1933

### Amendment 21
Repeal of 18th amendment
1933

### Amendment 22
President limited to two terms
1951

### Amendment 23
Presidential electors for District of Columbia
1961

### Amendment 24
Abolition of poll tax (tax paid for opportunity to vote) as requirement for voting in federal elections
1964

### Amendment 25
Orderly transfer of power when a President becomes disabled
1967

### Amendment 26
Suffrage for citizens 18 years and older
1971

### Amendment 27
Restrictions on changes in Congressional salaries
1992

# How a Bill Becomes a Law

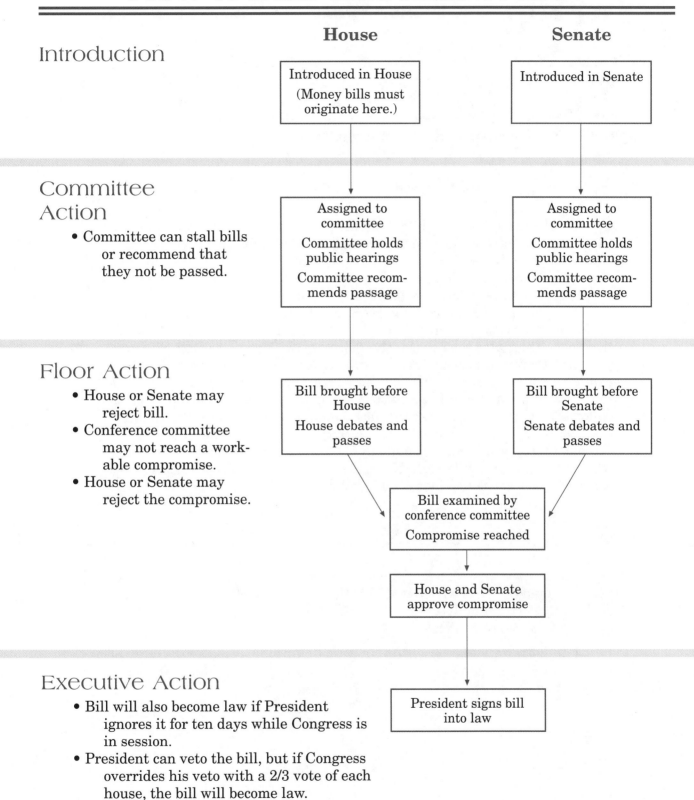

**House**      **Senate**

Introduction

> Introduced in House
> (Money bills must
> originate here.)

> Introduced in Senate

Committee
Action

- Committee can stall bills
  or recommend that
  they not be passed.

> Assigned to
> committee
>
> Committee holds
> public hearings
>
> Committee recom-
> mends passage

> Assigned to
> committee
>
> Committee holds
> public hearings
>
> Committee recom-
> mends passage

Floor Action

- House or Senate may
  reject bill.
- Conference committee
  may not reach a work-
  able compromise.
- House or Senate may
  reject the compromise.

> Bill brought before
> House
>
> House debates and
> passes

> Bill brought before
> Senate
>
> Senate debates and
> passes

> Bill examined by
> conference committee
>
> Compromise reached

> House and Senate
> approve compromise

Executive Action

- Bill will also become law if President
  ignores it for ten days while Congress is
  in session.
- President can veto the bill, but if Congress
  overrides his veto with a 2/3 vote of each
  house, the bill will become law.
- If President ignores bill and Congress
  adjourns within 10 days, the bill is dead.
  This is the "pocket veto."

> President signs bill
> into law

# CURRENT EXECUTIVE OFFICIALS

**President:** _____

    **Address:** The White House, Washington, D.C. 20500

**Vice President:** _____

    **Address:** The United States Senate, Washington, D.C. 20510

## Electing a President and Vice President

Presidents and their Vice Presidents are elected through a system called the *electoral college,* a group of men and women representing their own states. Each state has the same number of electoral votes as it has senators and representatives in Congress. The District of Columbia has 3 electoral votes. Today, the electoral college has 538 members.

Candidates for President and Vice President are chosen by political parties at a national convention in the late summer of the Presidential election year. The states then choose their electors, each party selecting its own.

On *election day (the first Tuesday after the first Monday in November),* voters go to the polls and choose a group of electors represented by the Presidential and Vice Presidential candidates whose names appear on the ballot. The party that receives the most popular votes wins all the electoral votes for that state. In December, the electors meet to cast their ballots. Although the electors are not bound by the popular vote, their vote generally reflects the popular vote cast in November. A majority of 270 electoral votes is needed to elect the President and Vice President.

## Inauguration Day

The inauguration of a new President takes place on the Capitol grounds late in January. The newly elected President, with his left hand on an open Bible and his right hand raised, recites the Presidential oath before the Chief Justice of the Supreme Court:

I do solemnly swear (or affirm) that I will faithfully execute the office of President of the United States, and will, to the best of my ability, preserve, protect, and defend the Constitution of the United States.

# United States Presidents

☆☆☆☆ *Memorize the Presidents in order.* ☆☆☆☆

| No. | Name | Born/Died | Years in Office | State of Birth | State of Residence When Elected |
|---|---|---|---|---|---|
| 1 | George Washington | 1732–1799 | 1789–1797 | Va. | Va. |
| 2 | John Adams | 1735–1826 | 1797–1801 | Mass. | Mass. |
| 3 | Thomas Jefferson | 1743–1826 | 1801–1809 | Va. | Va. |
| 4 | James Madison | 1751–1836 | 1809–1817 | Va. | Va. |
| 5 | James Monroe | 1758–1831 | 1817–1825 | Va. | Va. |
| 6 | John Quincy Adams | 1767–1848 | 1825–1829 | Mass. | Mass. |
| 7 | Andrew Jackson | 1767–1845 | 1829–1837 | S.C. | Tenn. |
| 8 | Martin Van Buren | 1782–1862 | 1837–1841 | N.Y. | N.Y. |
| 9 | William Henry Harrison | 1773–1841 | 1841 | Va. | Ohio |
| 10 | John Tyler | 1790–1862 | 1841–1845 | Va. | Va. |
| 11 | James K. Polk | 1795–1849 | 1845–1849 | N.C. | Tenn. |
| 12 | Zachary Taylor | 1784–1850 | 1849–1850 | Va. | La. |
| 13 | Millard Fillmore | 1800–1874 | 1850–1853 | N.Y. | N.Y. |
| 14 | Franklin Pierce | 1804–1869 | 1853–1857 | N.H. | N.H. |
| 15 | James Buchanan | 1791–1868 | 1857–1861 | Pa. | Pa. |
| 16 | Abraham Lincoln | 1809–1865 | 1861–1865 | Ky. | Ill. |
| 17 | Andrew Johnson | 1808–1875 | 1865–1869 | N.C. | Tenn. |
| 18 | Ulysses S. Grant | 1822–1885 | 1869–1877 | Ohio | Ill. |
| 19 | Rutherford B. Hayes | 1822–1893 | 1877–1881 | Ohio | Ohio |
| 20 | James A. Garfield | 1831–1881 | 1881 | Ohio | Ohio |
| 21 | Chester A. Arthur | 1830–1886 | 1881–1885 | Vt. | N.Y. |
| 22 | Grover Cleveland | 1837–1908 | 1885–1889 | N.J. | N.Y. |
| 23 | Benjamin Harrison | 1833–1901 | 1889–1893 | Ohio | Ind. |
| 24 | Grover Cleveland | 1837–1908 | 1893–1897 | N.J. | N.J. |
| 25 | William McKinley | 1843–1901 | 1897–1901 | Ohio | Ohio |
| 26 | Theodore Roosevelt | 1858–1919 | 1901–1909 | N.Y. | N.Y. |
| 27 | William Howard Taft | 1857–1930 | 1909–1913 | Ohio | Ohio |
| 28 | Woodrow Wilson | 1856–1924 | 1913–1921 | Va. | N.J. |

| No. | Name | Born/Died | Years in Office | State of Birth | State of Residence when Elected |
|-----|------|-----------|-----------------|----------------|---------------------------------|
| 29 | Warren G. Harding | 1865–1923 | 1921–1923 | Ohio | Ohio |
| 30 | Calvin Coolidge | 1872–1933 | 1923–1929 | Vt. | Mass. |
| 31 | Herbert Hoover | 1874–1964 | 1929–1933 | Iowa | Calif. |
| 32 | Franklin D. Roosevelt | 1882–1945 | 1933–1945 | N.Y. | N.Y. |
| 33 | Harry S. Truman | 1884–1972 | 1945–1953 | Mo. | Mo. |
| 34 | Dwight D. Eisenhower | 1890–1969 | 1953–1961 | Tex. | N.Y. |
| 35 | John F. Kennedy | 1917–1963 | 1961–1963 | Mass. | Mass. |
| 36 | Lyndon B. Johnson | 1908–1973 | 1963–1969 | Tex. | Tex. |
| 37 | Richard M. Nixon | 1913–1994 | 1969–1974 | Calif. | Calif. |
| 38 | Gerald R. Ford | 1913– | 1974–1977 | Nebr. | Mich. |
| 39 | James E. Carter | 1924– | 1977–1981 | Ga. | Ga. |
| 40 | Ronald W. Reagan | 1911– | 1981–1989 | Ill. | Calif. |
| 41 | George H. Bush | 1924– | 1989–1993 | Mass. | Tex. |
| 42 | William J. Clinton | 1946– | 1993– | Ark. | Ark. |

*The White House*

## Past Presidents

(name and years in office; list only once)

| Who have served in my lifetime | Who have served since my father or mother was born | Who have served since one of my grand-parents was born |
| --- | --- | --- |
| | | |
| | | |
| | | |
| | | |
| | | |
| | | |
| | | |
| | | |

## Vice Presidents Who Became Presidents

| By Election | By Death of President |
| --- | --- |
| John Adams<br>Thomas Jefferson<br>Martin Van Buren<br>Theodore Roosevelt<br>Calvin Coolidge<br>Harry S. Truman<br>Lyndon B. Johnson<br>Richard M. Nixon<br>George H. Bush | John Tyler (William H. Harrison—pneumonia)<br>Millard Fillmore (Zachary Taylor—heat stroke)<br>Andrew Johnson (Abraham Lincoln—assassination)<br>Chester A. Arthur (James A. Garfield—assassination)<br>Theodore Roosevelt (William McKinley—assassination)<br>Calvin Coolidge (Warren G. Harding—undetermined illness)<br>Harry S. Truman (Franklin D. Roosevelt—cerebral hemorrhage)<br>Lyndon B. Johnson (John F. Kennedy—assassination) |

Gerald Ford, who had been *appointed* to the Vice Presidency upon resignation of Spiro T. Agnew, became President when Richard Nixon resigned from office.

# The President's Cabinet

Because the President has such an important and difficult job to perform, he selects many assistants. The departmental heads that work closest with the President are known collectively as the cabinet. Cabinet members must be approved by the Senate.

| Executive Department/Head (Write name of current official in blank.) | Purpose |
|---|---|
| **1. Dept. of State** <br><br> _____ <br> Secretary of State | • handle foreign affairs |
| **2. Dept. of Treasury** <br><br> _____ <br> Secretary of the Treasury | • handle finances of federal government, print/coin money, and operate Secret Service, Bureau of Narcotics, and Internal Revenue Service |
| **3. Dept. of Defense** <br><br> _____ <br> Secretary of Defense | • supervise armed forces and oversee development and purchase of weapons |
| **4. Dept. of Justice** <br><br> _____ <br> Attorney General | • direct federal court system, prosecute violations of federal laws, supervise federal penitentiary system and Federal Bureau of Investigation, and direct Immigration and Naturalization Service |
| **5. Dept. of the Interior** <br><br> _____ <br> Secretary of the Interior | • supervise national bureaus responsible for public lands and national parks, natural resources and their conservation, geologic surveys, mines, Indian affairs, and overseas territories |
| **6. Dept. of Agriculture** <br><br> _____ <br> Secretary of Agriculture | • research and test new products, supervise meat inspection, enforce federal farm laws, and manage national forests |
| **7. Dept. of Commerce** <br><br> _____ <br> Secretary of Commerce | • operate National Weather Service, issue patents and registers trademarks, conduct federal census every ten years, set weight and measures standards, supervise and promote domestic and international commerce and shipping |

| Executive Department/Head<br>(Write name of current official in blank.) | Purpose |
|---|---|
| **8. Dept. of Labor**<br><br>_____<br>Secretary of Labor | • supervise government's employment programs, unemployment insurance, and enforcement of Fair Labor Standards Act |
| **9. Dept. of Health and Human Services**<br><br>_____<br>Secretary of Health and Human Services | • administer Social Security Administration, Food and Drug Administration, and Public Health Service |
| **10. Dept. of Housing and Urban Development**<br><br>_____<br>Secretary of Housing and Urban Development | • oversee departments that deal with public transportation, housing development, urban renewal, and related programs |
| **11. Dept. of Transportation**<br><br>_____<br>Secretary of Transportation | • supervise agencies dealing with transportation and research causes of major airplane and train wrecks |
| **12. Dept. of Energy**<br><br>_____<br>Secretary of Energy | • consolidate various energy agencies |
| **13. Dept. of Education**<br><br>_____<br>Secretary of Education | • supervise various educational programs of other agencies as well as oversee Office of Education |
| **14. Dept. of Veteran's Affairs**<br><br>_____<br>Secretary of Veteran Affairs | • promotes the welfare of veterans of the U.S. armed forces |

# CURRENT LEGISLATIVE OFFICIALS

**Speaker of the House:** _____

    **Address:** House of Representatives, Washington, D.C. 20515

**President of the Senate:** _____

    **Address:** House of Representatives, Washington, D.C. 20510

**U.S. Senators for my state**

  1. Name: _____

     Address: _____

  2. Name: _____

     Address: _____

**U.S. Representative for my area**

    Name: _____

    Address: _____

## Apportionment of House Seats by State
### (Consult an almanac.)

|  | |  | |  | |
|---|---|---|---|---|---|
| Ala. | _____ | La. | _____ | Ohio | _____ |
| Alaska | _____ | Maine | _____ | Okla. | _____ |
| Ariz. | _____ | Md. | _____ | Oreg. | _____ |
| Ark. | _____ | Mass. | _____ | Pa. | _____ |
| Calif. | _____ | Mich. | _____ | R.I. | _____ |
| Colo. | _____ | Minn. | _____ | S.C. | _____ |
| Conn. | _____ | Miss. | _____ | S.Dak. | _____ |
| Del. | _____ | Mo. | _____ | Tenn. | _____ |
| Fla. | _____ | Mont. | _____ | Tex. | _____ |
| Ga. | _____ | Nebr. | _____ | Utah | _____ |
| Hawaii | _____ | Nev. | _____ | Vt. | _____ |
| Idaho | _____ | N.H. | _____ | Va. | _____ |
| Ill. | _____ | N.J. | _____ | Wash. | _____ |
| Ind. | _____ | N.Mex. | _____ | W.Va. | _____ |
| Iowa | _____ | N.Y. | _____ | Wis. | _____ |
| Kans. | _____ | N.C. | _____ | Wyo. | _____ |
| Ky. | _____ | N.Dak. | _____ | | |

# CURRENT SUPREME COURT JUSTICES

**Chief Justice:** _____

    **Address:** The Supreme Court, Washington, D.C. 20543

**Associate Justices**

1. _____

2. _____

3. _____

4. _____

5. _____

6. _____

7. _____

8. _____

## Past Chief Justices of the Supreme Court

| Dates Served | Chief Justice | Appointed By |
|---|---|---|
| 1789–1795 | John Jay | G. Washington |
| 1795–1795 | John Rutledge | G. Washington |
| 1796–1800 | Oliver Ellsworth | G. Washington |
| 1801–1835 | John Marshall | J. Adams |
| 1836–1864 | Roger Brooke Taney | A. Jackson |
| 1864–1873 | Salmon Portland Chase | A. Lincoln |
| 1874–1888 | Morrison Remick Waite | U. S. Grant |
| 1888–1910 | Melville Weston Fuller | G. Cleveland |
| 1910–1921 | Edward Douglass White | W. Taft |
| 1921–1930 | William Howard Taft | W. Harding |
| 1930–1941 | Charles Evans Hughes | H. Hoover |
| 1941–1946 | Harlan Fiske Stone | F. D. Roosevelt |
| 1946–1953 | Frederick Moore Vinson | H. Truman |
| 1953–1969 | Earl Warren | D. Eisenhower |
| 1969–1986 | Warren E. Burger | R. Nixon |
| 1986– | William Rehnquist | R. Reagan |

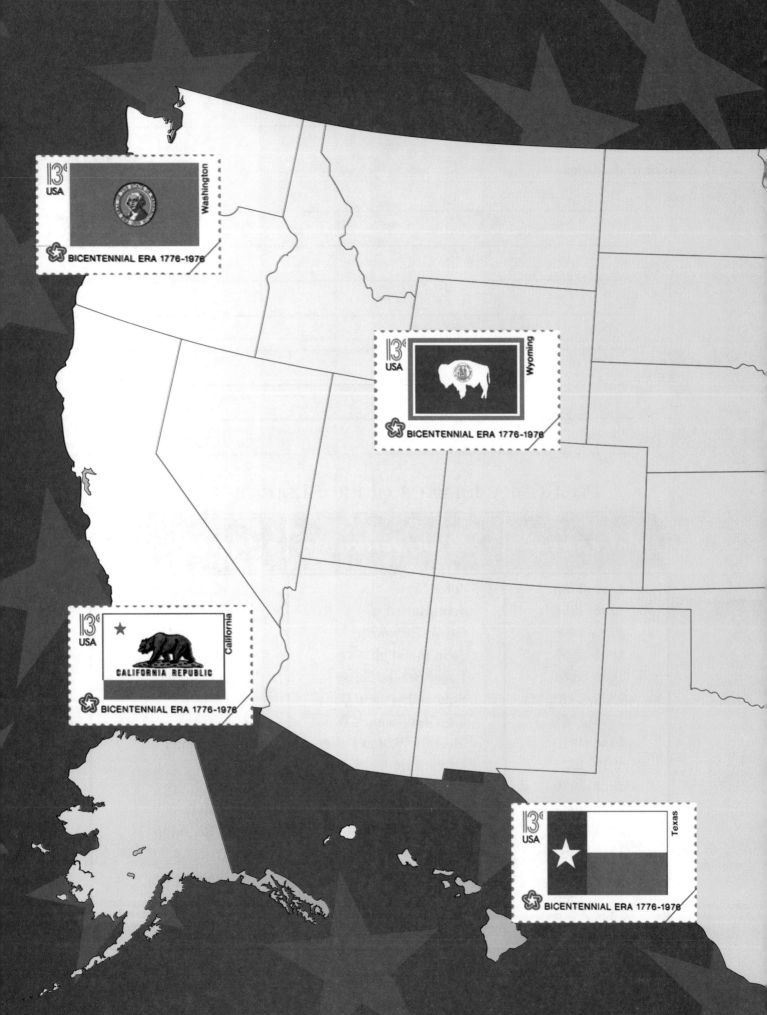

# PART TWO

# State Studies

# CONTENTS

**Introduction** ................................................ 35

**State Symbols** ........................................ 37

**Geography** .............................................. 43
    Climate ................................................ 44
    Wildlife ................................................ 45
    Plant Life .............................................. 49
    Natural Resources ................................ 52
    Industries ............................................. 54
    Highlights and Attractions ................. 55

**Transportation** ...................................... 57

**History** .................................................... 58
    Native Americans ................................ 58
    Time Line ............................................. 59
    Important People .................................. 60

**Government** ............................................. 62

# MY STATE: _____
(state)

## Introduction

**Meaning of name:** _____

_____

**Union entry date:** _____ **Order of admission:** _____

**Region:** _____

**Boundaries**

    North: _____     East: _____

    South: _____     West: _____

**Area:** _____ sq. mi. **Population:** _____

**Rank in area:** _____     **Rank in population:** _____
<br>(among the 50 states)                      (among the 50 states)

| *Largest Cities* | *Population* |
|---|---|
| **Capital:** _____ | |
| **Other cities:** | |
|   1. _____ | |
|   2. _____ | |
|   3. _____ | |
|   4. _____ | |
|   5. _____ | |
|   6. _____ | |
|   7. _____ | |
|   8. _____ | |
|   9. _____ | |
|  10. _____ | |

# Location

*Label and color your state on the map below. Label its neighbors with a different color.*

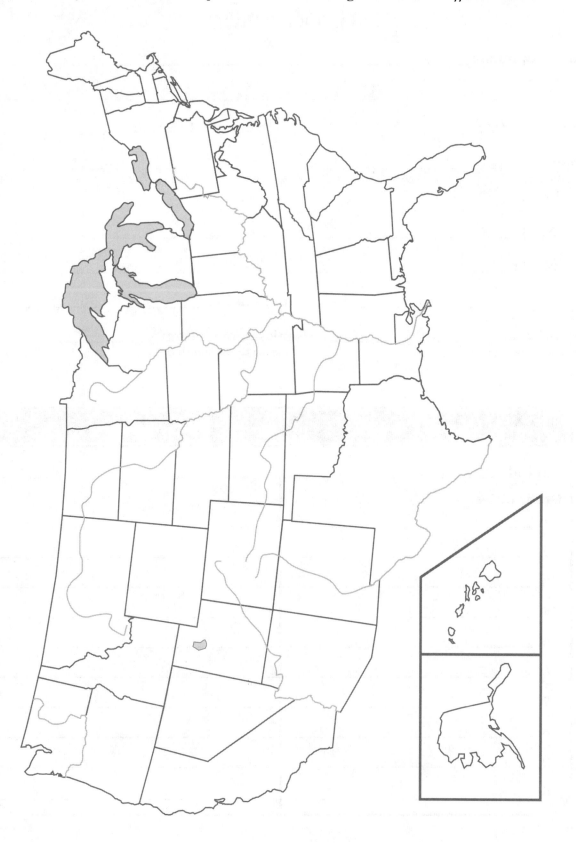

# SYMBOLS OF _____

## State Nickname: _____

Just like some people, states have nicknames in addition to their real names.

Nicknames reveal some unique feature of a state.  My state's nickname was probably

chosen because _____

_____

_____

_____

_____

_____

_____

_____

## State Motto: "_____

_____"

A state's motto reveals the goals of its people.  My state's motto was probably

chosen because _____

_____

_____

_____

_____

_____

_____

_____

State Flower: _____

---

Photo or drawing

---

**Description:** _____

_____

_____

**Where found:** _____

_____

_____

**Why chosen:** _____

_____

_____

_____

State Tree:_____

Photo or drawing

Description:_____
_____
_____

Where found: _____
_____
_____

Why chosen: _____
_____
_____
_____

State Bird: _____

```
┌─────────────────────────────────────────────┐
│ Photo or drawing                            │
│                                             │
│                                             │
│                                             │
│                                             │
│                                             │
│                                             │
│                                             │
│                                             │
│                                             │
│                                             │
│                                             │
│                                             │
└─────────────────────────────────────────────┘
```

**Description:**_____

_____

_____

**Where found:** _____

_____

_____

**Why chosen:** _____

_____

_____

_____

State Song: _____
(title)

by _____
(composer)

*Write the lyrics to the state song here:*

_____

_____

_____

_____

_____

_____

_____

_____

_____

_____

_____

_____

_____

_____

_____

_____

_____

_____

_____

_____

## State Flag: *Draw a picture of the state flag and explain any interesting features.*

_____

_____

_____

_____

_____

_____

_____

| Photo or drawing |
| :-- |
| |

## State Seal: *Trace the state seal and explain any significant symbols.*

| Photo or drawing |
| :-- |
| |

_____

_____

_____

_____

_____

_____

_____

_____

*Make a map of the state. Use the symbols suggested on page 3. Label the state capital and a few important cities and towns as well as major lakes, rivers, mountains, etc. Also label some well-known parks, resorts, and attractions.*

# State Climate

**General description:** _____

_____

_____

_____

**Record temperatures**

    High: _____    Low: _____

**Record precipitation:** _____

**Special climatic features:** _____

_____

_____

_____

## Average Temperatures and Precipitation

| Month | Temperature Highs | Lows | Precipitation |
|---|---|---|---|
| January | | | |
| February | | | |
| March | | | |
| April | | | |
| May | | | |
| June | | | |
| July | | | |
| August | | | |
| September | | | |
| October | | | |
| November | | | |
| December | | | |

# State Wildlife

## Mammals

1. **Name:** _____

   Description: _____

   _____

   _____

   _____

   _____

2. **Name:** _____

   Description: _____

   _____

   _____

   _____

   _____

3. **Name:** _____

   Description: _____

   _____

   _____

   _____

   _____

4. **Name:** _____

   Description: _____

   _____

   _____

   _____

   _____

# Birds

**1. Name:** _____

Description: _____

_____

_____

_____

_____

**2. Name:** _____

Description: _____

_____

_____

_____

_____

**3. Name:** _____

Description: _____

_____

_____

_____

_____

**4. Name:** _____

Description: _____

_____

_____

_____

_____

# Reptiles and Amphibians

**1. Name:** _____

Description: _____

_____

_____

_____

_____

**2. Name:** _____

Description: _____

_____

_____

_____

_____

**3. Name:** _____

Description: _____

_____

_____

_____

_____

**4. Name:** _____

Description: _____

_____

_____

_____

_____

Fish

1. **Name:** _____

   Description: _____

   _____

   _____

   _____

   _____

2. **Name:** _____

   Description: _____

   _____

   _____

   _____

   _____

3. **Name:** _____

   Description: _____

   _____

   _____

   _____

   _____

4. **Name:** _____

   Description: _____

   _____

   _____

   _____

   _____

# State Plant Life

Flowers

**1. Name:** _____

Description: _____

_____

_____

_____

_____

**2. Name:** _____

Description: _____

_____

_____

_____

_____

**3. Name:** _____

Description: _____

_____

_____

_____

_____

**4. Name:** _____

Description: _____

_____

_____

_____

_____

# Trees

**1. Name:** _____

   Description: _____

   _____

   _____

   _____

   _____

**2. Name:** _____

   Description: _____

   _____

   _____

   _____

   _____

**3. Name:** _____

   Description: _____

   _____

   _____

   _____

   _____

**4. Name:** _____

   Description: _____

   _____

   _____

   _____

   _____

## Other Plants

**1. Name:** _____

Description: _____

_____

_____

_____

_____

**2. Name:** _____

Description: _____

_____

_____

_____

_____

**3. Name:** _____

Description: _____

_____

_____

_____

_____

**4. Name:** _____

Description: _____

_____

_____

_____

_____

# Natural Resources in _____

God has blessed our nation with many valuable natural resources. Some states are rich in mineral wealth such as oil or coal. Others boast acres of fine timber for lumbering or fertile soil for farming. A state's resources may include minerals, timber, soil, fish and other seafoods, water power, furs, or any combination of these and other natural bounties. Natural resources largely determine the major industries in a region.

**Resources that were once important in my state:** _____

_____

_____

_____

_____

**Resources in my state that are important today:** _____

_____

_____

_____

_____

Photo or drawing

# State Resource and Industry Map

*Make a map of the state's natural resources and industries. Use the symbols suggested on page 3. Also label seaports and a few important cities for reference.*

# Industries in _____
(state)

Industries keep our nation's economy afloat by providing jobs, goods, and services for most Americans. A state's industries are usually closely related to its natural resources. Most states have a wide variety of industries ranging from tourism and other service industries to agriculture, manufacturing, and mining.

**Early important industries:** _____

_____

_____

_____

_____

_____

**Important industries today:** _____

_____

_____

_____

_____

_____

**Chief exports:** _____

_____

_____

_____

**Important seaports:** _____

_____

_____

_____

# State Highlights and Attractions

## Parks and Recreation Areas

| Name | Location | Special Attractions |
|------|----------|---------------------|
|      |          |                     |
|      |          |                     |
|      |          |                     |
|      |          |                     |
|      |          |                     |
|      |          |                     |

## Museums *(list largest ones first)*

| Name | Location | Special Attractions |
|------|----------|---------------------|
|      |          |                     |
|      |          |                     |
|      |          |                     |
|      |          |                     |
|      |          |                     |
|      |          |                     |

## Amusement Parks and Resorts

| Name | Location | Special Attractions |
|---|---|---|
|  |  |  |
|  |  |  |
|  |  |  |
|  |  |  |
|  |  |  |
|  |  |  |

## Other Attractions

| Name | Location | Special Attractions |
|---|---|---|
|  |  |  |
|  |  |  |
|  |  |  |
|  |  |  |
|  |  |  |
|  |  |  |

# TRANSPORTATION IN _____
(state)

*Refer to the key below and learn the meaning of the different map symbols. Find one of each on a road map of the state.*

| (64) National Interstate Highway | (2) State and Provincial Highway |
|---|---|
| (20) U.S. Highway | Trans-Canada Highway |
| | (85) Mexican and Central American Highway |

*Refer to a road map of the state to figure the distance between cities in the state. The exercise below shows you how to figure time.*

|  | city | city | miles | time |
|---|---|---|---|---|
| **1.** From | _____ | to _____ | = _____ | _____ |
| **2.** From | _____ | to _____ | = _____ | _____ |
| **3.** From | _____ | to _____ | = _____ | _____ |
| **4.** From | _____ | to _____ | = _____ | _____ |
| **5.** From | _____ | to _____ | = _____ | _____ |

*To compute the amount of time it would take to travel in a car between two cities, you must divide. For this exercise, we will use 60 as the divisor, although the speed limit may be different in your state. (1) Copy the number of miles between the cities you listed above, beneath the word* miles. *(2) Work the problems below. (3) Place your answers (the quotient) on the correct lines above, beneath the word* time.

**1.** 60 | _____ miles          **2.** 60 | _____ miles

**3.** 60 | _____ miles          **4.** 60 | _____ miles

**5.** 60 | _____ miles

_____
(state)

## Native American Heritage

_Write about the native Americans who lived in the state long ago._

**Tribe:** _____

    Location: _____

    Description: _____

    _____

    _____

**Tribe:** _____

    Location: _____

    Description: _____

    _____

    _____

**Tribe:** _____

    Location: _____

    Description: _____

    _____

    _____

**Tribe:** _____

    Location: _____

    Description: _____

    _____

    _____

# Time Line of State History

*Fill in the time line with significant historical events.*

| Year | Event | Significance |
|------|-------|--------------|
|      |       |              |
|      |       |              |
|      |       |              |
|      |       |              |
|      |       |              |
|      |       |              |
|      |       |              |
|      |       |              |
|      |       |              |
|      |       |              |
|      |       |              |
|      |       |              |
|      |       |              |
|      |       |              |
|      |       |              |

# Important People from _____
(state)

**Name:** _____

_____

Time period: _____

Noted for: _____

_____

_____

_____

_____

_____

_____

Photo or drawing

Photo or drawing

**Name:** _____

_____

Time period: _____

Noted for: _____

_____

_____

_____

_____

_____

_____

**Name:** _____

_____

Time period: _____

Noted for: _____

_____

_____

_____

_____

_____

_____

Photo or drawing

Photo or drawing

**Name:** _____

_____

Time period: _____

Noted for: _____

_____

_____

_____

_____

_____

_____

**Governor**

Name: _____

Address: _____

_____

_____

How chosen: _____

_____

_____

_____

_____

_____

**Past four governors**

1. _____

2. _____

3. _____

4. _____

Photo or drawing of governor's mansion

# United States Congress

**U.S. Senators**

Name: _____

Address: _____

_____

Name: _____

Address: _____

_____

**U.S. Representative for my area**

Name: _____

Address: _____

_____

# State Legislators

**State Senators**

Name: _____

Address: _____

_____

**State Representatives**

**for my district**

Name: _____

Address: _____

_____

**others**

Name: _____

Address: _____

_____

Name: _____

Address: _____

_____

Name: _____

Address: _____

_____

Name: _____

Address: _____

_____

Name: _____

Address: _____

_____

Name: _____

Address: _____

_____

# Past Important Government Leaders from My State

Name: _____    Name: _____

Office: _____    Office: _____

Noted for: _____    Noted for: _____

_____    _____

_____    _____

_____    _____

_____    _____

Photo or drawing of state capitol building

Scenes from around the state

# Local Studies

# Part Three

# CONTENTS

**County** ............................................................... **69**

    Buildings ........................................................... 70

    Officials ............................................................. 70

**Geography** ........................................................ **71**

    Weather .............................................................. 72

    Natural Resources ............................................. 73

    Industries .......................................................... 75

    Highlights and Attractions ................................ 76

**City** ...................................................................... **78**

    Buildings ........................................................... 79

    Officials ............................................................. 79

**Local History** .................................................. **81**

**Family History** ................................................ **82**

# MY COUNTY:

(parish or borough) _____ (name)

Meaning of name: _____

_____

County seat: _____

What makes my county special: _____

_____

_____

_____

_____

_____

_____

Photo or drawing

# County Buildings (addresses)

**Courthouse:** _____

_____

**Judicial Building:** _____

_____

**Sheriff's Department:** _____

_____

**Voter Registration Office:** _____

_____

**Tag Office:** _____

_____

**Others:** _____

_____

_____

_____

# County Officials (names)

**County Administrator:** _____

**Sheriff:** _____

**Supervisor of Elections:** _____

**Tax Collector:** _____

**Superintendent of Schools:** _____

**Others:** _____

_____

_____

_____

# LOCAL GEOGRAPHY

Map of _____
(county)

*Make a map of your county.  Label the county seat and any important cities or towns as well as mountains, lakes, rivers, etc.  Also label any well-known parks, resorts, and attractions.*

# Local Weather

*Record the local weather conditions over a two-week period.*

## Week of _____

| Date | Temperature Highs | Lows | Precipitation | Wind Speed |
|------|------|------|------|------|
|      |      |      |      |      |
|      |      |      |      |      |
|      |      |      |      |      |
|      |      |      |      |      |
|      |      |      |      |      |
|      |      |      |      |      |
|      |      |      |      |      |

## Week of _____

| Date | Temperature Highs | Lows | Precipitation | Wind Speed |
|------|------|------|------|------|
|      |      |      |      |      |
|      |      |      |      |      |
|      |      |      |      |      |
|      |      |      |      |      |
|      |      |      |      |      |
|      |      |      |      |      |
|      |      |      |      |      |

# Natural Resources in _____

**Resources that were once important:** _____

_____

_____

_____

_____

_____

**Resources that are important today:** _____

_____

_____

_____

_____

_____

Photo or drawing

# Local Resource and Industry Map

*Make a map of the county's natural resources and industries. Use the symbols suggested on page 3. Also label a few important cities for reference.*

# Industries in _____

**Early important industries:** _____

_____

_____

_____

_____

_____

_____

_____

_____

**Important industries today:** _____

_____

_____

_____

_____

_____

_____

_____

_____

# Local Highlights and Attractions

## Parks and Recreation Areas

| Name | Location | Special Attractions |
|------|----------|---------------------|
|      |          |                     |
|      |          |                     |
|      |          |                     |
|      |          |                     |
|      |          |                     |
|      |          |                     |

## Important Museums

| Name | Location | Special Attractions |
|------|----------|---------------------|
|      |          |                     |
|      |          |                     |
|      |          |                     |
|      |          |                     |
|      |          |                     |
|      |          |                     |

## Amusement Parks and Resorts

| Name | Location | Special Attractions |
|---|---|---|
|  |  |  |
|  |  |  |
|  |  |  |
|  |  |  |
|  |  |  |

## Other Local Attractions

| Name | Location | Special Attractions |
|---|---|---|
|  |  |  |
|  |  |  |
|  |  |  |
|  |  |  |
|  |  |  |

# MY CITY/TOWN: _____
(metropolitan area)

**Meaning of name:** _____

_____

**What makes my city/town special:** _____

_____

_____

_____

_____

_____

_____

_____

_____

_____

```
Photo or drawing




```

# City (Metro) Buildings (addresses)

**Police Department:** _____

_____

**Fire Department:** _____

_____

**Post Office:** _____

_____

**Library:** _____

_____

**My Church:** _____

_____

**My School:** _____

_____

**Others:** _____

_____

_____

# City (Metro) Officials (names)

**Mayor or City Manager:** _____

**Police Chief:** _____

**Fire Chief:** _____

**My Pastor:** _____

**My Principal:** _____

**Others:** _____

_____

_____

# Map of _____

*Make a simple map of the city/town. Label your church, school, library, courthouse, police station, fire department, and other important locations.*

## Time Line of Local History
### (county or city)

| Year | Event | Significance |
|------|-------|--------------|
|      |       |              |
|      |       |              |
|      |       |              |
|      |       |              |
|      |       |              |
|      |       |              |
|      |       |              |
|      |       |              |
|      |       |              |
|      |       |              |
|      |       |              |
|      |       |              |
|      |       |              |
|      |       |              |
|      |       |              |
|      |       |              |
|      |       |              |
|      |       |              |
|      |       |              |
|      |       |              |
|      |       |              |

# My Family History

*Write about your family history. Where were your parents born? Where were you born? In what parts of the state or country have you lived?*

**My great grandparents:** _____

_____

_____

_____

_____

_____

**My grandparents:** _____

_____

_____

_____

_____

_____

**My parents:** _____

_____

_____

_____

_____

**Myself:** _____

_____

_____

_____

_____

Family photos

# State Profiles

★ ★ ★

# Alabama

*The Heart of Dixie*

## Symbols

**Other nicknames:** Cotton State, Yellowhammer State
**Motto:** "We dare defend our rights"
**Bird:** Yellowhammer
**Flower:** Camellia
**Tree:** Southern pine
**Stone:** Marble
**Mineral:** Hematite
**Fish:** Tarpon
**Song:** "Alabama"

## Geography

**Area:** 51,705 sq. mi.
**Highest point:** Cheaha Mt. (2,407 ft.)

**Major mountains:**
- Appalachians

**Major rivers:**
- Mobile
- Tombigbee
- Tennessee
- Alabama

**Major lakes:**
- William "Bill" Dannelly Reservoir

## Profile

**Date/Order of admission:** 1819 (22nd)
**Abbreviations:** Ala., AL
**Capital:** Montgomery
**Population:** 4,062,608 (1990)
**Major cities:**
- Birmingham
- Huntsville
- Mobile

**Famous for:**
- swamps and bayous
- Gulf Coast beaches
- Booker T. Washington
- Wilson and Wheeler Dams
- Mound State Monument
- Tuskegee University
- Sequoyah Cave
- Marshall Space Flight Center
- Redstone Arsenal

# Alaska

*The Last Frontier*

## Symbols

**Other nicknames:** Land of the Midnight Sun, Great Land
**Motto:** "North to the Future"
**Flower:** Blue forget-me-not
**Tree:** Sitka spruce
**Bird:** Willow ptarmigan
**Fish:** King Salmon
**Song:** "Alaska's Flag"
**Gem:** Jade

## Geography

**Area:** 591,004 sq. mi.
**Highest point:** Mt. McKinley (20,320 ft.)
**Major mountains:**
- Alaska Range
- Brooks Range

**Major river:** Yukon
**Major islands:**
- Kodiak Island
- Aleutian Islands

## Profile

**Date/Order of admission:** 1959 (49th)
**Abbreviation:** AK
**Capital:** Juneau
**Population:** 551,947 (1990)
**Major cities:**
- Anchorage
- Fairbanks
- Nome

**Famous for:**
- gold, oil, other minerals
- salmon and king crab
- whales and seals
- Eskimos and igloos
- Trans-Alaska Pipeline
- active volcanoes
- Glacier Bay National Park
- Point Barrow, most northerly point in U.S.

# Arizona

*The Grand Canyon State*

## Symbols

**Motto:** "God enriches"
**Bird:** Cactus wren
**Tree:** Paloverde
**Flower:** Saguaro cactus blossom
**Gem:** Turquoise
**Song:** "Arizona"

## Geography

**Area:** 114,000 sq. mi.
**Highest point:** Humphrey's Peak (12,679 ft.)
**Major mountains:**
- San Francisco Peaks
- White
- Gila

**Major rivers:**
- Colorado
- Little Colorado
- Gila

**Major lakes:**
- Mohave
- Havasu
- Mead

## Profile

**Date/Order of admission:** 1912 (48th)
**Abbreviations:** Ariz., AZ
**Population:** 3,677,985 (1990)
**Capital:** Phoenix
**Major cities:**
- Tucson
- Flagstaff

**Famous for:**
- American Indian reservations
- Saguaro National Monument
- Painted desert
- Apache Trail
- Hoover Dam
- Petrified forest
- deserts
- Grand Canyon
- Hopi Indians
- copper
- Meteor Crater

# Arkansas

*The Land of Opportunity*

## Symbols

**Motto:** "The people rule"
**Flower:** Apple blossom
**Stone:** Diamond
**Bird:** Mockingbird
**Tree:** Pine
**Song:** "Arkansas"

## Geography

**Area:** 53,187 sq. mi.
**Highest point:** Magazine Mt. (2,753 ft.)
**Major mountains:**
- Ozarks
- Ouachita

**Major lakes:**
- Chicot
- Millwood
- Ouachita
- Bull Shoals

**Major rivers:**
- Arkansas
- Red
- Ouachita
- Mississippi

## Profile

**Date/Order of admission:** 1836 (25th)
**Abbreviations:** Ark., AR
**Population:** 2,362,239 (1990)
**Capital:** Little Rock
**Major cities:**
- North Little Rock
- Pine Bluff
- Fort Smith

**Famous for:**
- Ozarks
- Hot Springs National Park
- diamonds
- Blanchard Springs Caverns
- bauxite (source of aluminum)
- rice
- Eureka Springs

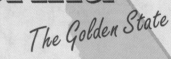

---

# California

*The Golden State*

## Symbols

**Motto:** "I have found it" (*Eureka*)
**Flower:** California (golden) poppy
**Bird:** California valley quail
**Tree:** California redwood
**Animal:** California grizzly bear
**Fish:** Sough Forke golden trout
**Marine mammal:** California gray whale
**Song:** "I Love You, California"
**Stone:** Serpentine          **Mineral:** Native gold

## Geography

**Area:** 158,706 sq. mi.
**Highest point:**
- Mt. Whitney (14,494 ft.)

**Major mountains:**
- Sierra Nevada
- Coast Ranges

**Major lakes:**
- Clear
- Tahoe
- Shasta
- Salton Sea

**Major rivers:**
- Sacramento
- San Joaquin

## Profile

**Date/Order of admission:** 1850 (31st)
**Abbreviations:** Calif., CA
**Population:** 29,839,250 (1990)
**Capital:** Sacramento
**Major cities:**
- Los Angeles
- San Francisco
- San Diego
- Anaheim
- Oakland
- Fresno

**Famous for:**
- beaches
- Hollywood
- earthquakes
- Spanish missions
- giant redwoods
- Golden Gate Bridge
- deserts
- Disneyland
- Death Valley
- Knott's Berry Farm
- 1849 gold rush
- Yosemite National Park

# Colorado
*The Centennial State*

## Symbols

**Motto:** "Nothing without Providence"
**Bird:** Lark bunting
**Flower:** Rocky Mountain columbine
**Tree:** Blue spruce
**Stone:** Aquamarine
**Animal:** Bighorn sheep
**Song:** "Where the Columbines Grow"

## Geography

**Area:** 104,091 sq. mi.
**Highest point:** Mt. Elbert (14,431 ft.)
**Major mountains:** Colorado Rockies
**Major lake:** Granby
**Major rivers:**
- Colorado
- Arkansas
- South Platte

## Profile

**Date/Order of
admission:** 1876 (38th)
**Abbreviations:** Colo., CO
**Population:** 3,307,912 (1990)
**Capital:** Denver
**Major cities:**
- Colorado Springs
- Aurora
- Pueblo

**Famous for:**
- Rocky Mountains
- Air Force Academy
- ski resorts
- Garden of the Gods
- U.S. Mint
- aspens
- Continental Divide
- Pike's Peak and Royal Gorge
- Mesa Verde National Park

---

# Connecticut
*The Constitution State*

## Symbols

**Other nicknames:**
Land of Steady Habits, Nutmeg State
**Motto:** "He who transplanted still sustains"
**Bird:** Robin
**Flower:** Mountain laurel
**Tree:** White oak
**Insect:** Praying mantis
**Animal:** Sperm whale
**Song:** "Yankee Doodle"

## Geography

**Area:** 5,018 sq. mi.
**Highest point:** Mt. Frissell (2,380 ft.)
**Major mountains:** Taconic
**Major lake:** Candlewood
**Major rivers:**
- Connecticut
- Housatonic
- Thames

## Profile

**Date/Order of
admission:** 1788 (5th)
**Abbreviations:** Conn., CT
**Population:** 3,295,669
**Capital:** Hartford
**Major cities:**
- Bridgeport
- New Haven

**Famous for:**
- insurance companies
- U.S. Coast Guard Academy
- seaports
- colonial landmarks
- the "Charter Oak"
- "greens" (public parks)
- Yale
- Mark Twain Mansion
- the "Fundamental Orders
of Connecticut"

# Delaware
*The First State*

## Symbols
**Motto:** "Liberty and Independence"
**Bird:** Blue hen chicken
**Flower:** Peach blossom
**Tree:** American holly
**Insect:** Ladybug
**Song:** "Our Delaware"

## Geography
**Area:** 2,044 sq. mi.
**Highest point:**
- Ebright Road (442 ft.)

**Major river:**
- Delaware

## Profile
**Date/Order of
   admission:** 1787 (1st)
**Abbreviations:** Del., DE
**Population:** 668,696 (1990)
**Capital:** Dover
**Major cities:**
- Wilmington
- New Castle

**Famous for:**
- Great Cypress Swamp
- historical churches
- first Christmas Seal
- Zwaanendal Museum
- E. I. du Pont de Nemours
  & Company
- chickens
- chemicals

---

## Symbols

**Motto:** "In God we trust."
**Bird:** Mockingbird
**Flower:** Orange blossom
**Tree:** Sabal palm
**Stone:** Agatized coral
**Shell:** Horse conch
**Freshwater fish:** Largemouth bass
**Saltwater fish:** Sailfish
**Saltwater mammal:** Porpoise (dolphin)
**Marine mammal:** Manatee
**Animal:** Florida panther
**Beverage:** Orange juice
**Song:** "Swanee River" ("Old Folks at Home")

## Geography
**Area:** 58,664 sq. mi.
**Highest point:** Walton County (345 ft.)
**Major rivers:**
- St. Johns
- Apalachicola
- St. Marys
- Perdido
- Suwannee
- Kissimmee

**Major lake:** Okeechobee

# Florida
*The Sunshine State*

## Profile
**Date/Order of
   admission:** 1845 (27th)
**Abbreviations:** Fla., FL
**Population:** 13,003,362 (1990)
**Capital:** Tallahassee
**Major cities:**
- Miami
- St. Petersburg
- Fort Lauderdale
- Jacksonville
- Tampa
- Pensacola

**Famous for:**
- citrus fruits
- Cape Canaveral
- Cypress Gardens
- Florida Keys
- Everglades
- Disney World (Orlando)
- palm trees
- beaches
- alligators
- fishing

# Georgia
## The Empire State of the South

### Symbols
**Other nicknames:** Peach State, Cracker State
**Motto:** "Wisdom, justice, and moderation"
**Song:** "Georgia on My Mind"
**Flower:** Cherokee rose     **Bird:** Brown thrasher
**Fish:** Largemouth bass     **Tree:** Live oak

### Geography
**Area:** 58,910 sq. mi.
**Highest point:** Brasstown Bald (4,784 ft.)
**Major rivers:**
- Savannah
- St. Mary's
- Ogeechee
- Chattahoochee
- Altamaha
- Flint

**Major lakes:**
- Sidney Lanier
- Clark Hill
- Hartwell
- Seminole
- Sinclair

**Major mountains:**
- Blue Ridge (part of Appalachians)

### Profile
**Date/Order of admission:** 1788 (4th)
**Abbreviations:** Ga., GA
**Population:** 6,508,419 (1990)
**Capital:** Atlanta
**Major cities:**
- Columbus
- Savannah
- Macon

**Famous for:**
- red clay
- Jekyll Island
- Okefenokee Swamp
- Callaway Gardens
- Masters Golf Tournament
- Eli Whitney (cotton gin)
- *Gone with the Wind* (novel)
- historic Savannah
- General Sherman's March to the Sea

---

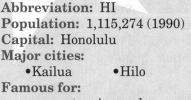

# Hawaii
## The Aloha State

### Symbols
**Motto:** "The life of the land is perpetuated in righteousness"
**Bird:** Nene (Hawaiian goose)
**Flower:** Hibiscus
**Tree:** Kukui (candlenut tree)
**Song:** "Hawaii Ponoi" ("Our Own Hawaii")

### Geography
**Area:** 6,471 sq. mi.
**Highest point:** Mauna Kea (13,796 ft.)
**Major islands:**
- Hawaii
- Maui
- Nihau
- Oahu
- Lanai
- Kauai

**Active volcanoes:**
- Mauna Loa
- Kilauea

**Major mountains:**
- Kawaikini
- Koolau Range
- Mauna Kea (volcano)
- Waianae Range

### Profile
**Date/Order of admission:** 1959 (50th)
**Abbreviation:** HI
**Population:** 1,115,274 (1990)
**Capital:** Honolulu
**Major cities:**
- Kailua
- Hilo

**Famous for:**
- coconuts, pineapples, sugar cane
- grass skirts, leis, luaus
- volcanoes
- macadamia nuts
- beaches and surfing
- orchids and hibiscus
- outrigger canoes
- Pearl Harbor
- Waikiki Beach

# Idaho
## The Gem State

## Symbols

**Motto:** "It is forever"
**Bird:** Mountain bluebird
**Flower:** Syringa
**Tree:** Western white pine
**Song:** "Here We Have Idaho"

## Geography

**Area:** 83,564 sq. mi.
**Highest point:** Borah Peak (12,662 ft.)
**Major rivers:**
- Snake
- Salmon
- Clearwater

**Major lakes:**
- Pend Oreille
- Coeur d'Alene

**Major mountains:**
- Salmon River
- Clearwater ⎤ parts of the Rockies
- Coeur d'Alene ⎦

## Profile

**Date/Order of
admission:** 1890 (43rd)
**Abbreviations:** Ida., ID
**Population:** 1,011,986 (1990)
**Capital:** Boise
**Major cities:**
- Idaho Falls
- Pocatello
- Twin Falls

**Famous for:**
- miners
- silver and lead
- Lava Hot Springs
- Crystal Ice Cave
- skiing
- The Steunenberg Trial
- potatoes
- Hell's Canyon

---

# Illinois
## The Prairie State

## Symbols

**Other nicknames:** Land of
Lincoln, Tall State
**Motto:** "State Sovereignty,
National Union"
**Bird:** Cardinal
**Flower:** Meadow violet
**Tree:** White oak
**Mineral:** Fluorite
**Animal:** White-tailed deer
**Song:** "Illinois"

## Geography

**Area:** 56,345 sq. mi.
**Highest point:** Charles Mound (1,235 ft.)
**Major rivers:**
- Mississippi
- Ohio
- Wabash
- Illinois

**Major lakes:**
- Michigan
- Carlyle

## Profile

**Date/Order of
admission:** 1818 (21st)
**Abbreviations:** Ill., IL
**Population:** 11,466,682 (1990)
**Capital:** Springfield
**Major cities:**
- Chicago
- Rockford
- Peoria
- East St. Louis

**Famous for:**
- corn
- Great Chicago Fire
- Fermi National Accelerator
- Chicago Mercantile Exchange
- world's first metal-frame skyscraper
- Dickson Mounds (Indian burial mounds)
- Sears Tower in Chicago
  (world's tallest building)

# Indiana

*The Hoosier State*

## Profile

**Date/Order of admission:** 1816 (19th)
**Abbreviations:** Ind., IN
**Population:** 5,564,228 (1990)
**Capital:** Indianapolis
**Major cities:**
- South Bend
- Fort Wayne
- Hammond
- Evansville

**Famous for:**
- corn
- steel mills
- oil refineries
- coal mines
- Wyandotte Cave
- Battle of Tippecanoe
- New Harmony
- Purdue University
- Indianapolis 500
- poet James Whitcomb Riley

## Symbols

**Motto:** "The Crossroads of America"
**Bird:** Cardinal
**Flower:** Peony
**Tree:** Tulip tree, or yellow poplar
**Stone:** Limestone
**Animal:** White-tailed deer
**Poem:** Indiana
**Song:** "On the Banks of the Wabash"

## Geography

**Area:** 36,185 sq. mi.
**Highest point:** Wayne County (1,257 ft.)
**Major rivers:**
- Wabash
- White
- Ohio

**Major lakes:**
- Michigan
- Monroe

---

# Iowa

*The Hawkeye State*

## Symbols

**Motto:** "Our liberties we prize and our rights we will maintain."
**Bird:** Eastern goldfinch
**Flower:** Wild rose
**Tree:** Oak
**Stone:** Geode
**Song:** "The Song of Iowa"

## Geography

**Area:** 56,275 sq. mi.
**Highest point:** Osceola County (1,658 ft.)
**Major rivers:**
- Mississippi
- Missouri

**Major lakes:**
- Coralville
- Red Rock
- Rathbun

## Profile

**Date/Order of admission:** 1846 (29th)
**Abbreviation:** IA
**Population:** 2,787,424 (1990)
**Capital:** Des Moines
**Major cities:**
- Cedar Rapids
- Davenport
- Sioux City
- Waterloo
- Dubuque

**Famous for:**
- Red Delicious apples
- The Pottawattamie County jail ("human squirrel cage")
- hot air balloons
- tulip festival
- farms
- Amana colonies

# Kansas

*The Sunflower State*

## Symbols

**Other nicknames:** Jayhawker State, Breadbasket of America
**Motto:** "To the stars through difficulties"
**Bird:** Western meadowlark
**Flower:** Sunflower
**Tree:** Cottonwood
**Animal:** American bison (buffalo)
**Song:** "Home on the Range"

## Geography

**Area:** 82,277 sq. mi.
**Highest point:** Wallace County (4,135 ft.)
**Major rivers:**
- Missouri
- Republican
- Kansas
- Smoky Hill
- Arkansas
- Cimarron

**Major lakes:**
- Tuttle Creek
- Milford
- Perry

## Profile

**Date/Order of admission:** 1861 (34th)
**Abbreviations:** Kans., KS
**Population:** 2,485,600 (1990)
**Capital:** Topeka
**Major cities:**
- Wichita
- Kansas City

**Famous for:**
- wheat
- oil and natural gas
- sunflowers
- hot plains
- Dodge City
- cattle
- salt
- *The Wizard of Oz*

---

## Symbols

**Motto:** "United we stand, divided we fall."
**Bird:** Cardinal
**Flower:** Goldenrod
**Tree:** Coffee tree
**Fish:** Bass
**Animal:** Gray squirrel
**Song:** "My Old Kentucky Home"

## Geography

**Area:** 40,409 sq. mi.
**Highest point:** Black Mountain (4,145 ft.)
**Major mountains:**
- Cumberland } parts of the
- Pine            Appalachians

**Major rivers:**
- Mississippi
- Ohio
- Tennessee

**Major lakes:**
- Kentucky Reservoir and other lakes formed by dams built by Tennessee Valley Authority

# Kentucky

*The Bluegrass State*

## Profile

**Date/Order of admission:** 1792 (15th)
**Abbreviations:** Ky., KY
**Population:** 3,698,969 (1990)
**Capital:** Frankfort
**Major cities:**
- Louisville
- Lexington
- Covington

**Famous for:**
- Boonesborough
- horses
- bluegrass
- Kentucky Derby
- Cumberland Falls
- Mammoth Cave
- Natural Bridge
- Fort Knox

# Louisiana

*The Pelican State*

## Symbols

**Motto:** "Union, Justice, and Confidence"
**Dog:** Catahoula leopard dog
**Fossil:** Petrified palmwood
**Song:** "Give Me Louisiana," "You Are My Sunshine"
**Bird:** Brown pelican  **Flower:** Magnolia
**Tree:** Bald cypress  **Gem:** Agate

## Geography

**Area:** 48,752 sq. mi.
**Highest point:** Driskill Mountain (535 ft.)
**Major rivers:**
- Red  • Sabine  • Mississippi

**Major lakes:**
- Sabine  • Toledo Bend  • Pontchartrain
- Calcasieu  Reservoir  • Borgne

## Profile

**Date/Order of admission:** 1812 (18th)
**Abbreviations:** La., LA
**Population:** 4,238,216 (1990)
**Capital:** Baton Rouge
**Major cities:**
- New Orleans  • Lake Charles
- Shreveport

**Famous for:**
- New Orleans jazz
- swamps and bayous
- Mardi Gras festival
- alligators
- chickory coffee
- Battle of New Orleans
- Cajun and Creole cuisine
- parishes (counties)

---

# Maine

*The Pine Tree State*

## Symbols

**Motto:** "I guide."
**Bird:** Chickadee
**Flower:** White pine cone and tassel
**Mineral:** Tourmaline
**Fish:** Landlocked salmon
**Song:** "State of Maine Song"
**Tree:** White pine  **Animal:** Moose

## Geography

**Area:** 33,265 sq. mi.
**Highest point:**
- Mt. Katahdin (5,268 ft.)

**Major mountains:**
- White (part of the Appalachians)

**Major rivers:**
- Androscoggin  • Penobscot
- Kennebec  • Saint John

**Major lakes:**
- Moosehead  • Sebago

## Profile

**Date/Order of admission:** 1820 (23rd)
**Abbreviation:** ME
**Population:** 1,233,223 (1990)
**Capital:** Augusta
**Major cities:**
- Portland  • Lewiston  • Bangor

**Famous for:**
- Acadia National Park
- lighthouses
- many rivers and streams
- Mt. Katahdin
- lobsters, sardines, and clams
- West Quoddy Head
- fishing villages and potato farms
- shipbuilding
- forests

# Maryland

*The Old Line State*

## Symbols

**Other nickname:** Free State
**Motto:** "Manly deeds, womanly words"
**Song:** "Maryland, My Maryland"
**Tree:** White oak     **Bird:** Baltimore oriole
**Fish:** Striped bass   **Flower:** Black-eyed Susan

## Geography

**Area:** 10,460 sq. mi.
**Highest point:** Backbone Mountain (3,360 ft.)
**Major mountains:**

- Blue Ridge } parts of the
- Allegheny } Appalachians

**Major rivers:**
- Potomac      • Susquehanna
- Patuxent     • Chester

**Major lakes:**
- Deep Creek   • Patapsco

## Profile

**Date/Order of admission:** 1788 (7th)
**Abbreviations:** Md., MD
**Population:** 4,798,622 (1990)
**Capital:** Annapolis
**Major city:** Baltimore
**Famous for:**
- Battle of Antietam (1862)
- U.S. Naval Academy at Annapolis
- steel mills
- America's first telegraph line (from Baltimore to Washington, D.C.)
- Mason-Dixon Line
- *Tom Thumb* (first American coal-burning steam locomotive)

---

# Massachusetts

*The Bay State*

## Symbols

**Other nickname:** Old Colony
**Motto:** "With the sword she seeks peace under liberty."
**Bird:** Black-capped chickadee
**Song:** "All Hail to Massachusetts"
**Mineral:** Babingtonite
**Fish:** Cod        **Horse:** Morgan
**Tree:** American elm   **Flower:** Mayflower

## Geography

**Area:** 8,284 sq. mi.
**Highest point:** Mt. Greylock (3,491 ft.)

**Major mountains:**
- Berkshire Hills   • Taconic

**Major rivers:**
- Connecticut      • Charles

**Major lakes:**
- Quabbin Reservoir
- Wachusett Reservoir

## Profile

**Date/Order of admission:** 1788 (6th)
**Abbreviations:** Mass., MA
**Population:** 6,029,051 (1990)
**Capital:** Boston
**Major cities:**
- Worcester    • Springfield

**Famous for:**
- sewing machine (Elias Howe)
- telephone (Alexander Graham Bell)
- Minuteman National Historical Park
- cranberries, cod, haddock
- Lexington, Concord, and Bunker Hill
- Nantucket Island and Martha's Vineyard
- Old Sturbridge Village    • Cape Cod
- Plymouth Plantation       • Harvard

# Michigan

*The Wolverine State*

## Symbols

**Motto:** "If you seek a pleasant peninsula, look around you."
**Song:** "Michigan, My Michigan"
**Bird:** Robin    **Flower:** Apple blossom
**Tree:** White pine    **Stone:** Petosky
**Gem:** Chlorastrolite    **Fish:** Trout

## Geography

**Area:** 58,527 sq. mi.
**Highest point:** Mt. Arvon (1,979 ft.)
**Major mountains:** Porcupine
**Major rivers:**
- Menominee
- Detroit
- St. Clair
- Grand

**Major lakes:**
- Superior
- Michigan
- Erie
- Huron

## Profile

**Date/Order of admission:** 1837 (26th)
**Abbreviations:** Mich., MI
**Population:** 9,238,784 (1990)
**Capital:** Lansing
**Major cities:**
- Detroit
- Grand Rapids
- Flint
- Saginaw

**Famous for:**
- over 11,000 lakes
- International Bridge at Sault Ste. Marie
- forests
- Isle Royale National Park
- tulip festival in Holland, Michigan
- Greenfield Village and Henry Ford Museum
- hunting, fishing, skiing, and other outdoor sports

---

# Minnesota

*The Gopher State*

## Symbols

**Other nicknames:** The North Star State, Land of 10,000 Lakes, Bread-and-Butter State, Land of the Sky-blue Waters, Theater of Seasons
**Flower:** Pink and white lady's slipper

**Motto:** "Star of the North"
**Bird:** Common loon
**Tree:** Norway, or red pine
**Gem:** Lake Superior agate
**Fish:** Walleye
**Song:** "Hail! Minnesota"

## Geography

**Area:** 84,402 sq. mi.
**Highest point:** Eagle Mountain (2,301 ft.)
**Major rivers:**
- Red River of the North
- Mississippi
- Rainy
- Minnesota

**Major lakes:**
- Red
- Leech
- Winnibigoshish
- Lake of the Woods
- Mille Lacs
- Superior

## Profile

**Date/Order of admission:** 1858 (32nd)
**Abbreviations:** Minn., MN
**Population:** 4,387,029 (1990)
**Capital:** St. Paul
**Major cities:**
- Minneapolis
- Duluth

**Famous for:**
- "Twin Cities" of Minneapolis and St. Paul
- Minnehaha Falls
- thousands of lakes
- winter carnivals and winter sports
- Voyageurs National Park
- Mayo Clinic
- Lake Itasca (source of the Mississippi)

---

# Mississippi

*The Magnolia State*

## Symbols

**Other nickname:** Bayou State
**Motto:** "By valor and arms"
**Bird:** Mockingbird
**Flower:** Magnolia
**Tree:** Magnolia
**Song:** "Go Mississippi"

## Geography

**Area:** 47,689 sq. mi.
**Highest point:** Woodall Mountain (806 ft.)
**Major rivers:**
- Mississippi
- Pascagoula
- Pearl
- Yazoo
- Big Black

**Major lakes:**
- Arkabutla
- Sardis
- Grenada
- Ross Barnett

## Profile

**Date/Order of admission:** 1817 (20th)
**Abbreviations:** Miss., MS
**Population:** 2,586,443 (1990)
**Capital:** Jackson
**Major cities:**
- Biloxi
- Gulfport
- Pascagoula

**Famous for:**
- cotton, petroleum
- magnolia trees
- bayous
- Eudora Welty
- Vicksburg National Military Park

---

# Missouri

*The Show Me State*

## Symbols

**Other nicknames:** Center State, Gateway to the West, Mother of the West
**Motto:** "The welfare of the people shall be the supreme law."

**Bird:** Eastern bluebird
**Flower:** Red hawthorn
**Tree:** Flowering dogwood
**Stone:** Mozarkite
**Song:** "Missouri Waltz"

## Geography

**Area:** 69,697 sq. mi.
**Highest point:** Taum Sauk Mountain (1,772 ft.)
**Major rivers:**
- Mississippi
- Missouri
- Osage

**Major lakes:**
- Lake of the Ozarks
- Table Rock
- Pomme de Terre
- Stockton

**Major mountains:** St. Francois

## Profile

**Date/Order of admission:** 1821 (24th)
**Abbreviations:** Mo., MO
**Population:** 5,137,804 (1990)
**Capital:** Jefferson City
**Major cities:**
- Kansas City
- Independence
- St. Louis
- St. Joseph

**Famous for:**
- author Mark Twain
- George Washington Carver (birthplace)
- Meramec Caverns
- Missouri Compromise of 1820
- outlaw Jesse James
- Gateway Arch in St. Louis
- Winston Churchill Memorial and Library
- Great Mississippi Steamboat Race in 1870

# Montana
*The Treasure State*

## Symbols

**Motto:** "Gold and silver"
**Bird:** Western meadowlark
**Flower:** Bitterroot
**Tree:** Ponderosa pine
**Animal:** Grizzly bear
**Fish:** Blackspotted cutthroat trout
**Grass:** Bluebunch wheat grass
**Stones:** Sapphire and agate
**Song:** "Montana"

## Geography

**Area:** 147,046 sq. mi.
**Highest point:** Granite Peak (12,850 ft.)
**Major mountains:** Rockies
**Major rivers:**
- Missouri
- Yellowstone

**Major lakes:**
- Flathead
- Fort Peck Reservoir

## Profile

**Date/Order of admission:** 1889 (41st)
**Abbreviations:** Mont., MT
**Population:** 803,655 (1990)
**Capital:** Helena
**Major cities:**
- Billings
- Great Falls

**Famous for:**
- rodeos
- cowboys and Indians
- "ghost towns"
- coal, copper, petroleum
- Medicine Rocks
- Giant Springs
- gold mining
- buffalo
- Custer's Last Stand

---

# Nebraska
*The Cornhusker State*

## Symbols

**Motto:** "Equality before the law"
**Bird:** Western meadowlark

**Flower:** Goldenrod
**Grass:** Little blue stem
**Tree:** Eastern cottonwood
**Fossil:** Mammoth
**Gem:** Blue agate
**Stone:** Prairie agate
**Song:** "Beautiful Nebraska"

## Geography

**Area:** 77,355 sq. mi.
**Highest point:** Kimball County (5,424 ft.)
**Major lake:** McConaughty
**Major rivers:**
- Missouri
- Platte
- Niobrara
- Republican

## Profile

**Date/Order of admission:** 1867 (37th)
**Abbreviations:** Nebr., NE
**Population:** 1,578,385 (1990)
**Capital:** Lincoln
**Major cities:**
- Omaha
- South Sioux City

**Famous for:**
- Buffalo Bill's home
- William Jennings Bryan
- part of the Oregon Trail
- meatpacking
- only state that has a unicameral legislature
- Boys Town
- stockyards
- Chimney Rock
- fossil beds

# Nevada
*The Silver State*

## Symbols

**Motto:** "All for our country"
**Bird:** Mountain bluebird
**Animal:** Desert bighorn sheep
**Song:** "Home Means Nevada"
**Grass:** Indian rice grass
**Flower:** Sagebrush   **Tree:** Single-leaf piñon
**Metal:** Silver   **Fossil:** Ichthyosaur

## Geography

**Area:** 110,561 sq. mi.
**Highest point:** Boundary Peak (13,140 ft.)
**Major rivers:**
- Humboldt
- Meadow Valley

**Major lakes:**
- Pyramid
- Mead
- Mohave

## Profile

**Date/Order of admission:** 1864 (36th)
**Abbreviations:** Nev., NV
**Population:** 1,201,833 (1990)
**Capital:** Carson City
**Major cities:**
- Las Vegas
- Reno

**Famous for:**
- Hoover Dam
- Lake Tahoe
- John Frémont and Kit Carson
- Lake Mead
- nuclear research
- deserts
- mining
- "ghost towns"
- gambling casinos
- less rainfall than any other state
- dude ranches and fishing resorts

---

# New Hampshire
*The Granite State*

## Symbols

**Motto:** "Live free or die"
**Bird:** Purple finch
**Flower:** Purple lilac
**Tree:** White birch
**Song:** "Old New Hampshire"

## Geography

**Area:** 9,279 sq. mi.
**Highest point:** Mount Washington (6,288 ft.)
**Major rivers:**
- Connecticut
- Merrimack
- Androscoggin

**Major lakes:**
- Winnipesaukee
- Sunapee

**Major mountains:**
- White

## Profile

**Date/Order of admission:** 1788 (9th)
**Abbreviations:** N.H., NH
**Population:** 1,113,915 (1990)
**Capital:** Concord
**Major cities:**
- Manchester
- Nashua
- Portsmouth

**Famous for:**
- Portsmouth naval shipyard
- Old Man of the Mountains (stone formation)
- Dartmouth College
- Daniel Webster   • Alan B. Shepard
- Hampton Beach   • granite
- leather   • Mount Washington
- dairy farms   • Cathedral of the Pines

# New Jersey

*The Garden State*

## Symbols

**Motto:** "Liberty and Prosperity"
**Bird:** Eastern goldfinch
**Flower:** Purple violet
**Tree:** Red oak
**Animal:** Horse

## Geography

**Area:** 7,787 sq. mi.

**Highest point:** High Point Mountain (1,801 ft.)
**Major rivers:**
- Hudson
- Delaware

**Major lake:**
- Hopatcong

**Major mountains:**
- Kittatinny

## Profile

**Date/Order of admission:** 1787 (3rd)
**Abbreviations:** N.J., NJ
**Population:** 7,748,634 (1990)
**Capital:** Trenton
**Major cities:**
- Newark
- Elizabeth
- Jersey City
- Paterson
- Camden

**Famous for:**
- seaside resorts
- chemical production
- Thomas Edison's laboratory at Menlo Park
- Atlantic City boardwalk
- Scene of nearly 100 battles in War for Independence
- George Washington Bridge

---

# New Mexico

*The Land of Enchantment*

## Symbols

**Motto:** "It grows as it goes"
**Bird:** Roadrunner

**Flower:** Yucca
**Tree:** Piñon
**Fish:** Cutthroat trout
**Animal:** Black bear
**Gem:** Turquoise
**Songs:** "Asi es Nuevo Mejico" and "O Fair New Mexico"

## Geography

**Area:** 121,593 sq. mi.
**Highest point:** Wheeler Peak (13,161 ft.)
**Major mountains:** Rockies
**Major lake:** Elephant Butte Reservoir
**Major rivers:**
- Rio Grande
- Pecos
- Canadian

## Profile

**Date/Order of admission:** 1912 (47th)
**Abbreviations:** N. Mex., NM
**Population:** 1,521,779 (1990)
**Capital:** Santa Fe
**Major cities:**
- Albuquerque
- Roswell

**Famous for:**
- mountain ranges, canyons, deserts
- Carlsbad Caverns National Park
- Santa Fe Trail
- rocket and nuclear energy research
- building and exploding first atomic bomb
- oil, uranium, and potash
- Kit Carson, Geronimo, Billy the Kid
- El Camino Real
- Santa Fe

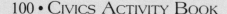

# New York

*The Empire State*

## Symbols

**Motto:** *Excelsior*, "Ever Upward."
**Song:** "I Love New York"
**Bird:** Bluebird          **Flower:** Rose
**Tree:** Sugar maple      **Fish:** Trout
**Gem:** Garnet            **Fruit:** Apple
**Animal:** Beaver         **Beverage:** Milk

## Geography

**Area:** 49,108 sq. mi.
**Highest point:** Mount Marcy (5,344 ft.)
**Major rivers:**
- Hudson
- Mohawk

**Major lakes:**
- Finger Lakes
- Champlain
- Erie
- Placid
- Oneida
- Ontairo

**Major mountains:**
- Adirondack
- Taconic
- Catskill

## Profile

**Date/Order of admission:** 1788 (11th)
**Abbreviations:** N.Y., NY
**Population:** 18,044,505 (1990)
**Capital:** Albany
**Major cities:**
- New York
- Buffalo
- Rochester
- Syracuse

**Famous for:**
- Empire State Building
- Statue of Liberty
- UN Headquarters
- Wall Street
- America's leader in banking, communication, finance, transportation
- New York City—largest city in United States
- Erie Canal
- Niagara Falls

# North Carolina

*The Tar Heel State*

## Symbols

**Motto:** "To be rather than to seem"
**Song:** "The Old North State"
**Mammal:** Gray squirrel
**Bird:** Cardinal          **Flower:** Dogwood
**Tree:** Pine             **Fish:** Channel bass
**Gem:** Emerald          **Rock:** Granite

## Geography

**Area:** 52,669 sq. mi.
**Highest point:** Mount Mitchell (6,684 ft.)

**Major rivers:**
- Roanoke
- Tar
- Neuse
- Cape Fear
- Yadkin
- Catawba

**Major lake:**
- Mattamuskeet

**Major mountains:**
- Blue Ridge
- Great Smoky

## Profile

**Date/Order of admission:** 1789 (12th)
**Abbreviations:** N.C., NC
**Population:** 6,657,630 (1990)
**Capital:** Raleigh
**Major cities:**
- Charlotte
- Winston-Salem
- Durham
- Greensboro

**Famous for:**
- Ocracoke Island (hideout of Blackbeard the pirate)
- textiles, tobacco, and wooden furniture
- Kitty Hawk
- Cape Hatteras ("Graveyard of the Atlantic")
- Blue Ridge Parkway
- Biltmore Estate

# North Dakota

## *The Flickertail State*

### Symbols

**Motto:** "Liberty and union, now and forever, one and inseparable."
**Bird:** Western meadowlark

**Flower:** Wild prairie rose
**Tree:** American elm
**Grass:** Western wheat grass
**Stone:** Teredo petrified wood
**Fish:** Northern pike
**Song:** "North Dakota Hymn"

### Geography

**Area:** 70,702 sq. mi.
**Highest point:** White Butte (3,506 ft.)
**Major rivers:**
- Souris
- Sheyenne
- Red River of the North
- Missouri
- James

**Major lakes:**
- Oahe
- Devils
- Sakakawea

### Profile

**Date/Order of admission:** 1889 (39th)
**Abbreviations:** N.Dak., ND
**Population:** 641,364 (1990)
**Capital:** Bismark
**Major cities:**
- Fargo
- Grand Forks
- Minot

**Famous for:**
- the Badlands
- wheat and cattle
- geographical center of North America near Rugby
- Theodore Roosevelt National Memorial Park
- Writing Rock
- Red River Valley—one of the world's most fertile farming areas

---

# Ohio

## *The Buckeye State*

### Symbols

**Motto:** "With God, all things are possible."
**Bird:** Cardinal
**Flower:** Scarlet carnation
**Tree:** Buckeye tree
**Beverage:** Tomato juice
**Stone:** Ohio flint
**Song:** "Beautiful Ohio"

### Geography

**Area:** 41,330 sq. mi.
**Highest point:** Campbell Hill (1,550 ft.)
**Major lake:** Erie
**Major mountains:** Allegheny
**Major rivers:**
- Maumee
- Scioto
- Ohio
- Miami
- Muskingum

### Profile

**Date/Order of admission:** 1803 (17th)
**Abbreviations:** Ohio, OH
**Population:** 10,887,325 (1990)
**Capital:** Columbus
**Major cities:**
- Toledo
- Cleveland
- Dayton
- Cincinnati

**Famous for:**
- Football Hall of Fame
- B. F. Goodrich (tires)
- Great Serpent Mound
- Neil Armstrong and John Glenn (astronauts)
- factories and farms
- oil wells
- wheat and corn
- *McGuffey Readers*

# Oklahoma

*The Sooner State*

## Symbols

**Motto:** "Labor conquers all things."
**Bird:** Scissor-tailed flycatcher
**Animal:** American buffalo
**Stone:** Barite rose (rose rock)
**Poem:** "Howdy Folks"  **Song:** "Oklahoma!"
**Flower:** Mistletoe  **Tree:** Redbud
**Fish:** White bass  **Grass:** Indian grass

## Geography

**Area:** 69,956 sq. mi.
**Highest point:** Black Mesa (4,973 ft.)
**Major rivers:**
- Arkansas
- Red

**Major lakes:**
- Texoma
- Lake O' the Cherokee

**Major mountains:**
- Ozarks
- Quachita
- Wichita (Gypsum Hills, Sandstone Hills)

## Profile

**Date/Order of admission:** 1907 (46th)
**Abbreviations:** Okla., OK
**Population:** 3,157,604 (1990)
**Capital:** Oklahoma City
**Major city:** Tulsa
**Famous for:**
- cowboys and rodeos
- Will Rogers
- the Chisolm Trail
- *Oklahoma!* (musical)
- Jim Thorpe
- crops and livestock
- oil wells
- beef and wheat
- *The Grapes of Wrath* (novel)
- manufacturing and mining

---

# Oregon

*The Beaver State*

## Symbols

**Motto:** "The union"
**Bird:** Western meadowlark
**Flower:** Oregon grape
**Tree:** Douglas fir
**Fish:** Chinook salmon
**Animal:** Beaver
**Stone:** Thunderegg
**Song:** "Oregon, My Oregon"

## Geography

**Area:** 97,073 sq. mi.
**Highest point:** Mount Hood (11,245 ft.)
**Major rivers:**
- Columbia
- John Day
- Willamette
- Snake

**Major lakes:**
- Upper Klamath
- Harney
- Crater
- Malheur

**Major mountains:**
- Cascade
- Blue
- Coast

## Profile

**Date/Order of admission:** 1859 (33rd)
**Abbreviations:** Oreg., OR
**Population:** 2,853,733 (1990)
**Capital:** Salem
**Major cities:**
- Portland
- Eugene

**Famous for:**
- Oregon Trail
- Crater Lake
- lumber and furs
- Columbia Gorge
- Hells Canyon
- Mount Hood
- evergreen forests
- hunting and fishing
- Sea Lion Caves
- Oregon Caves National Monument

# Pennsylvania

*The Keystone State*

## Symbols

**Motto:** "Virtue, liberty, and independence"
**Bird:** Ruffed grouse
**Flower:** Mountain laurel
**Tree:** Eastern hemlock
**Fish:** Brook trout
**Animal:** White-tailed deer

## Geography

**Area:** 45,308 sq. mi.
**Highest point:** Mount Davis (3,213 ft.)

**Major rivers:**
- Delaware
- Allegheny
- Susquehanna
- Ohio

**Major lakes:**
- Pymatuning
- Erie
- Wallenpaupack

**Major mountains:**
- Appalachian
- Allegheny

## Profile

**Date/Order of admission:** 1787 (2nd)
**Abbreviations:** Pa., PA
**Population:** 11,924,710 (1990)
**Capital:** Harrisburg
**Major cities:**
- Philadelphia
- Pittsburgh
- Erie

**Famous for:**
- U.S. Mint
- Pennsylvania Dutch
- Valley Forge
- Amish communities
- steel
- Mason-Dixon Line
- Liberty Bell
- Independence Hall
- mining and shipbuilding
- Pennsylvania Turnpike
- William Penn and the Quakers
- Hershey, PA (world's largest chocolate factory)

# Rhode Island

*The Ocean State*

## Symbols

**Motto:** "Hope"
**Bird:** Rhode Island Red
**Flower:** Violet
**Tree:** Red maple
**Rock:** Cumberlandite
**Mineral:** Bowenite
**Song:** "Rhode Island"

## Geography

**Area:** 1,212 sq. mi.
**Highest point:** Jerimoth Hill (812 ft.)
**Major rivers:**
- Blackstone
- Pautuxet
- Pawcatuck

**Major lake:**
- Scituate Reservoir

## Profile

**Date/Order of admission:** 1790 (13th)
**Abbreviations:** R.I., RI
**Population:** 1,005,984 (1990)
**Capital:** Providence
**Major cities:**
- Warwick
- Newport

**Famous for:**
- fishing
- Tennis Hall of Fame
- colonial buildings
- first Baptist meeting house
- Samuel Slater, founder of the American textile industry
- manufacturing, jewelry, spout silverware

# South Carolina

*The Palmetto State*

## Symbols

**Motto:** "While I breathe, I hope."
**Flower:** Yellow jessamine, or "Carolina"

**Bird:** Carolina wren
**Tree:** Palmetto
**Gem:** Amethyst
**Fish:** Striped bass
**Animal:** White-tailed deer
**Song:** "Carolina"

## Geography

**Area:** 31,113 sq. mi.

**Highest point:**
- Sassafras Mountain (3,560 ft.)

**Major rivers:**
- Pee Dee
- Santee
- Savannah

**Major lakes:**
- Marion
- Clark Hill Reservoir
- Moultrie
- Hartman Reservoir

## Profile

**Date/Order of admission:** 1788 (8th)
**Abbreviations:** S.C., SC
**Population:** 3,505,707 (1990)
**Capital:** Columbia
**Major cities:**
- Charleston
- Greenville
- Spartanburg

**Famous for:**
- Revolutionary and Civil War battles
- first Southern state to leave the Union
- Francis Marion ("Swamp Fox")
- Charlestowne Landing
- textiles and peaches
- Charleston
- Magnolia Gardens
- Myrtle Beach
- Cypress Gardens
- Hilton Head
- John C. Calhoun
- plantations
- rice and indigo

---

# South Dakota

*The Sunshine State*

## Symbols

**Motto:** "Under God the people rule."

**Bird:** Ring-necked pheasant
**Flower:** Pasqueflower
**Tree:** Black hills spruce
**Grass:** Western wheat grass
**Gem:** Fairburn agate
**Fish:** Walleye
**Animal:** Coyote
**Mineral:** Rose quartz
**Song:** "Hail, South Dakota"

## Geography

**Area:** 77,116 sq. mi.
**Highest point:** Harney Peak (7,242 ft.)
**Major rivers:** Missouri and its tributaries
**Major lakes:**
- Oahe
- Lewis and Clark
- Francis Case

## Profile

**Date/Order of admission:** 1889 (40th)
**Abbreviations:** S.Dak., SD
**Population:** 699,999 (1990)
**Capital:** Pierre
**Major cities:**
- Sioux Falls
- Rapid City
- Aberdeen

**Famous for:**
- coyotes
- Mount Rushmore
- Wild Bill Hickok
- Indian Reservations
- Sitting Bull
- Black Hills
- gold-mining
- Sioux chief Crazy Horse
- manufacturing and tourism
- Wind Cave National Park
- Fort Randall Dam
- Laura Ingalls Wilder

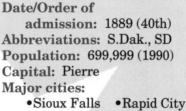

# Tennessee

*The Volunteer State*

## Symbols

**Motto:** "Agriculture and Commerce"
**Animal:** Raccoon
**Song:** "My Homeland Tennessee"
**Bird:** Mockingbird    **Flower:** Iris
**Tree:** Tulip poplar    **Rock:** Limestone
**Stone:** Agate    **Gem:** Tennessee pearl

## Geography

**Area:** 42,114 sq. mi.

**Highest point:**
- Clingmans Dome (6,643 ft.)

**Major rivers:**
- Tennessee    • Cumberland
- Mississippi

**Major lakes:**
- Kentucky Reservoir and other lakes formed by dams built by Tennessee Valley Authority

## Profile

**Date/Order of admission:** 1796 (16th)
**Abbreviations:** Tenn., TN
**Population:** 4,896,641 (1990)
**Capital:** Nashville
**Major cities:**
- Memphis    • Knoxville
- Chattanooga    • Oak Ridge

**Famous for:**
- Civil War battlefields
- the Hermitage—home of Andrew Jackson
- Tennessee Valley Authority
- Oak Ridge, site of world's first nuclear reactor
- Grand Ole Opry
- Casey Jones
- Great Smoky Mountains National Park
- the Scopes "Monkey" Trial over evolution

# Texas

*The Lone Star State*

## Symbols

**Motto:** "Friendship"
**Bird:** Mockingbird

**Flower:** Bluebonnet
**Tree:** Pecan
**Stone:** Palmwood
**Gem:** Topaz
**Dish:** Chili
**Grass:** Sideoats grama
**Song:** "Texas, Our Texas"

## Geography

**Area:** 266,807 sq. mi.
**Highest point:** Guadalupe Peak (8,751 ft.)
**Major rivers:**
- Rio Grande    • Red
- Brazos    • Pecos

**Major lake:**
- Toledo Bend Reservoir

## Profile

**Date/Order of admission:** 1845 (28th)
**Abbreviations:** Tex., TX
**Population:** 17,059,805 (1990)
**Capital:** Austin
**Major cities:**
- El Paso    • Dallas-Forth Worth
- San Antonio    • Corpus-Christi
- Houston

**Famous for:**
- Lyndon B. Johnson Space Center
- John F. Kennedy's assassination in 1963
- Texas Longhorns    • ten-gallon hats
- Big Bend National Park    • chili
- Mexican heritage    • the King Ranch
- cattle and sheep    • cowboys
- the Alamo    • oil
- farms

# Utah

*The Beehive State*

## Symbols

**Motto:** "Industry"
**Bird:** California gull
**Flower:** Sego lily
**Tree:** Blue spruce
**Gem:** Topaz
**Song:** "Utah, We Love Thee"

## Geography

**Area:** 84,899 sq. mi.
**Highest point:** Kings Peak (13,498 ft.)
**Major rivers:**
- Colorado
- Green
- Sevier

**Major lakes:**
- Great Salt
- Powell

## Profile

**Date/Order of admission:** 1896 (45th)
**Abbreviations:** Utah, UT
**Population:** 1,727,784 (1990)
**Capital:** Salt Lake City
**Major city:** Ogden
**Famous for:**
- Great Salt Lake
- Bingham Canyon
- Zion National Park
- Great Salt Lake Desert
- salt flats
- Rocky Mountains
- Bryce Canyon National Park
- uranium
- Bonneville Speedway
- gold, copper
- first transcontinental railroad

# Vermont

*The Green Mountain State*

## Symbols

**Motto:** "Freedom and Unity"
**Bird:** Hermit thrush
**Flower:** Red clover
**Tree:** Sugar maple
**Animal:** Morgan horse
**Song:** "Hail, Vermont"

## Geography

**Area:** 9,614 sq. mi.
**Highest point:** Mount Mansfield (4,393 ft.)
**Major rivers:**
- Connecticut
- Otter Creek

**Major lake:**
- Champlain

**Major mountains:**
- Green
- Taconic

## Profile

**Date/Order of admission:** 1791 (14th)
**Abbreviations:** Vt., VT
**Population:** 564,964 (1990)
**Capital:** Montpelier
**Major cities:**
- Burlington
- Rutland

**Famous for:**
- granite, marble, talc
- maple syrup
- forests
- skiing
- Green Mountains
- Ethan Allen and the Green Mountain Boys in the War for Independence

# Virginia
*The Old Dominion*

## Symbols

**Motto:** "Ever thus to tyrants"
**Bird:** Cardinal
**Flower:** Dogwood
**Tree:** Dogwood
**Animal:** Foxhound
**Shell:** Oyster
**Song:** "Carry Me Back to Old Virginia"

## Geography

**Area:** 40,767 sq. mi.
**Highest point:** Mt. Rogers (5,729 ft.)
**Major rivers:**
- Potomac
- Rappahannock
- York
- James
- Shenandoah

**Major lake:**
- Smith Mountain

**Major mountains:**
- Blue Ridge

## Profile

**Date/Order of admission:** 1788 (10th)
**Abbreviations:** Va., VA
**Population:** 6,216,568 (1990)
**Capital:** Richmond
**Major cities:**
- Norfolk
- Virginia Beach
- Arlington
- Fairfax

**Famous for:**
- Monticello (Thomas Jefferson's home)
- Newport News (world's largest shipyard)
- many Revolutionary and Civil War battles
- Arlington National Cemetery
- Mt. Vernon (George Washington's home)
- James River plantations
- Appomattox Court House
- Jamestown
- Cumberland Gap
- Williamsburg
- Shenandoah Valley
- Robert E. Lee

---

# Washington
*The Evergreen State*

## Symbols

**Motto:** "By and by"
**Bird:** Willow goldfinch
**Tree:** Western hemlock
**Flower:** Rhododendron
**Fish:** Steelhead trout
**Gem:** Petrified wood
**Song:** "Washington My Home"

## Geography

**Area:** 68,139 sq. mi.
**Highest point:** Mt. Rainier (14,410 ft.)
**Major mountains:**
- Olympic
- Cascade
- Rockies

**Major rivers:**
- Columbia
- Spokane
- Snake
- Yakima

**Major lakes:**
- Chelan
- Franklin D. Roosevelt

## Profile

**Date/Order of admission:** 1889 (42nd)
**Abbreviations:** Wash., WA
**Population:** 4,887,941 (1990)
**Capital:** Olympia
**Major cities:**
- Seattle
- Spokane
- Tacoma

**Famous for:**
- Cascade Mountains
- apples and flower bulbs
- Olympic National Park
- Olympic Mountains
- Mount St. Helens (volcano)
- thick forests
- lumber
- skiing
- seafood
- Seattle Center
- Mount Rainier
- Space Needle
- Grand Coulee Dam

# West Virginia

BICENTENNIAL ERA 1776-1976

*The Mountain State*

## Symbols

**Motto:** "Mountaineers are always free."
**Bird:** Cardinal
**Flower:** Big rhododendron
**Tree:** Sugar maple
**Fish:** Brook trout
**Animal:** Black bear
**Songs:** "West Virginia, My Home Sweet Home"; "The West Virginia Hills"; "This Is My West Virginia"

## Geography

**Area:** 24,231 sq. mi.
**Highest point:** Spruce Knob (4,860 ft.)
**Major rivers:**
- Ohio
- Kanawha
- Potomac

**Major lake:**
- Bluestone Reservoir

## Profile

West Virginia USA 20c — Cardinal & Rhododendron Maximum

**Date/Order of admission:** 1863 (35th)
**Abbreviations:** W. Va., WV
**Population:** 1,801,625 (1990)
**Capital:** Charleston
**Major cities:**
- Clarksburg
- Huntington
- Wheeling
- Parkersburg

**Famous for:**
- John Brown's raid of the federal arsenal at Harper's Ferry
- making most of the glass marbles in America
- first to introduce rural free delivery
- forests of valuable hardwood
- glassware and pottery
- coal, natural gas, petroleum, rock salt, limestone, sand, clay, and shale

# Wisconsin

Wisconsin USA 20c — Robin & Wood Violet

13¢ USA Wisconsin — BICENTENNIAL ERA 1776-1976

*The Badger State*

## Symbols

**Motto:** "Forward."
**Flower:** Violet
**Rock:** Red granite
**Fish:** Muskellunge
**Song:** "On, Wisconsin!"
**Bird:** Robin
**Tree:** Sugar maple
**Mineral:** Galena
**Animal:** Badger

## Geography

**Area:** 56,153 sq. mi.
**Highest point:** Timms Hill (1,940 ft.)
**Major rivers:**
- Mississippi
- St. Croix
- Wisconsin
- Black
- Chippewa

**Major lakes:**
- Winnebago
- Pepin
- Poygan
- Mendota
- Michigan
- Superior

## Profile

**Date/Order of admission:** 1848 (30th)
**Abbreviations:** Wis., WI
**Population:** 4,906,745 (1990)
**Capital:** Madison
**Major cities:**
- Milwaukee
- Green Bay
- Racine

**Famous for:**
- cheese, butter, milk
- "America's Dairyland"
- turbines and engines
- paper and other forest products
- winter sports
- hunting and fishing

# Wyoming

*The Equality State*

 BICENTENNIAL ERA 1776-1976

## Symbols

*Western Meadowlark & Indian Paintbrush*

**Motto:** "Equal rights"
**Bird:** Meadowlark
**Flower:**
   Indian paintbrush
**Tree:** Cottonwood
**Stone:** Jade
**Bird:** Meadowlark
**Song:** "Wyoming"

## Profile

**Date/Order of
   admission:** 1890 (44th)
**Abbreviations:** Wyo., WY
**Population:** 455,975 (1990)
**Capital:** Cheyenne
**Major cities:**
   •Casper   •Laramie
**Famous for:**
   •Rocky Mountains
   •Fort Laramie National Historic Site
   •Guided Missile Launching Site
      (Warren Air Force Base)
   •Shoshone National Forest
   •Grand Teton National Park
   •Jackson Hole
   •Devil's tower
   •sheep
   •cattle
   •oil
   •rodeos
   •Old Faithful

## Geography

**Area:** 97,809 sq. mi.
**Highest point:** Gannett Peak (13,785 ft.)
**Major rivers:**
   •Green        •Yellowstone
   •North Platte
**Major lakes:**
   •Yellowstone
   •Flaming Gorge Reservoir
**Major mountains:**
   •Black Hills   •Bighorn
   •Laramie       •Absaroka
   •Grand Teton